D1436708

VECTOR METHODS

UNIVERSITY MATHEMATICAL TEXTS

GENERAL EDITORS

ALEXANDER C. AITKEN, D.Sc., F.R.S.
DANIEL E. RUTHERFORD, Dr. Math.

Other volumes in preparation

VECTOR METHODS

APPLIED TO DIFFERENTIAL
GEOMETRY, MECHANICS, AND
POTENTIAL THEORY

BY

D. E. RUTHERFORD
M.A., B.Sc. (St. And.), Dr. Math. (Amsterdam)
LECTURER IN APPLIED MATHEMATICS AT ST. ANDREWS UNIVERSITY

SIXTH EDITION
With 16 Figures

OLIVER AND BOYD
EDINBURGH AND LONDON
NEW YORK: INTERSCIENCE PUBLISHERS, INC.
1949

First Edition	.	.	1939
Second Edition	.	.	1943
Third Edition	.	.	1944
Fourth Edition	.	.	1946
Fifth Edition	.	.	1948
Sixth Edition	•	•	1949

PRINTED AND PUBLISHED IN GREAT BRITAIN BY
OLIVER AND BOYD LTD., EDINBURGH

PREFACE

THE Vector Calculus has in recent years acquired such a prominence in the equipment of the mathematical student, that it is now as indispensable a tool as are the Differential and Integral Calculi. The object of this book is to provide on the one hand a clear account of the abstract theory, and on the other a brief but broad survey of the applications of the theory to various branches of pure and applied Mathematics. The book is, of course, designed for the use of the undergraduate and it is not intended to compete with more specialised works, many of which are listed in the bibliography. I have, nevertheless, endeavoured to be as comprehensive as space permitted, but obviously completeness is unattainable in a work of this size. According to the needs of the student, the book can serve as a textbook for a course specifically on Vectors, or, where such a course is not available, it may be used as a handbook of reference throughout a series of courses.

Many friends have given me assistance and advice for which I am very grateful, but in particular I wish to thank Dr. C. A. Coulson, Mr. G. S. Rushbrooke and my wife for offering many valuable suggestions and for reading the proofs.   D. E. R.

ST. ANDREWS, *June* 1939

PREFACE TO THE SECOND EDITION

IN this edition the chapter on Mechanics has been rewritten and considerably extended. Elsewhere smaller revisions and additions have been made and it is hoped that the usefulness of the book has thereby been increased.

D. E. R.

ST. ANDREWS, *November* 1942

CONTENTS

vii

CHAPTER I

VECTOR ALGEBRA

§ **1.** WE are all familiar with the fact that if B is two miles from A and if C is two miles from B, then C is not necessarily four miles from A. Only in very special circumstances are distances compounded according to the ordinary arithmetical law of addition. Actually there are many other entities which behave in this way as distances rather than as ordinary numbers ; the study of such entities leads to the calculus of vectors.

A **scalar** is a quantity which has magnitude but which is not related to any definite direction in space. A scalar is completely specified by a number. A **vector** is an entity which obeys the same law of addition as a distance does. It has a magnitude and is also related to a definite direction in space. It follows that any vector may be represented by a straight line with an arrow head whose direction is that of the vector and whose length represents the magnitude of the vector according to a convenient scale. We shall denote vectors by Clarendon type, e.g., **r**. German textbooks usually use Gothic type to denote vectors. A vector of zero magnitude can have no direction associated with it. Such a vector is called the **zero vector** and is denoted by **0**. The magnitude of a vector is called its **length**. It is frequently convenient to denote the length of a vector **r** by r. A similar convention is used when vectors are denoted by other letters.

Two vectors are added in the same way as two distances, so we define the addition of vectors by the **parallelogram**

B

law. *If* **a** *is represented by the directed line* $\overline{OA}$ *and* **b** *is represented by* $\overline{OB}$, *then* **a** + **b** *is defined as the vector represented by* $\overline{OC}$ *where OACB is the completed parallelogram* (fig. 1). $\overline{OC}$ is the **sum** or **resultant** of $\overline{OA}$ and $\overline{OB}$. $\overline{AC}$

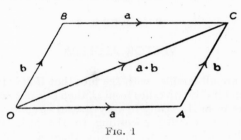

Fɪɢ. 1

has the same magnitude and direction as $\overline{OB}$, so we may alternatively choose $\overline{AC}$ to represent **b**. Thus, the resultant of $\overline{OA}$ and $\overline{AC}$ is $\overline{OC}$. If **a** + **b** = **0**, i.e. if O and C coincide, then **b** = − **a**. Thus − **a** is a vector which has the same length as **a** but the opposite direction. If **a** is represented by $\overline{OA}$, then − **a** is represented by $\overline{AO}$.

It is evident from definition that the **commutative law**

$$\mathbf{a} + \mathbf{b} = \mathbf{b} + \mathbf{a},$$

and the **associative law**

$$\mathbf{a} + (\mathbf{b} + \mathbf{c}) = (\mathbf{a} + \mathbf{b}) + \mathbf{c} = \mathbf{a} + \mathbf{b} + \mathbf{c},$$

both hold for the addition of vectors.

The vector **a** + **a** is naturally called 2**a** and is a vector in the same direction as **a** but of twice its length. Similarly $m\mathbf{a}$ is a vector in the same direction as **a** but of length ma. Evidently

$$m(n\mathbf{a}) = n(m\mathbf{a}) = nm\mathbf{a},$$

and

$$(m + n)\mathbf{a} = m\mathbf{a} + n\mathbf{a}.$$

Also from the similar triangles in fig. 2, we see that

$$m(\mathbf{a} + \mathbf{b}) = m\mathbf{a} + m\mathbf{b}.$$

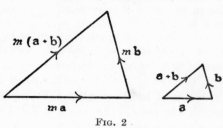

FIG. 2

If a vector $\mathbf{r}$ can be represented as a sum of vectors $\mathbf{a} + \mathbf{b} + \ldots + \mathbf{d}$, we say that $\mathbf{r}$ can be **resolved** into **components** $\mathbf{a}, \mathbf{b}, \ldots, \mathbf{d}$. It is important to realise that any vector can be resolved into three components in *any* three given directions which are not coplanar. If $\mathbf{r}$ is the given vector, we can construct a parallelepiped about $\mathbf{r}$ as diagonal, whose edges are parallel to the three given directions. Then $\mathbf{r} = \mathbf{a} + \mathbf{b} + \mathbf{c}$, where $\mathbf{a}, \mathbf{b}, \mathbf{c}$ are the vectors indicated in fig. 3. Further, this resolution is unique, for if

$$\mathbf{a}_1 + \mathbf{b}_1 + \mathbf{c}_1 = \mathbf{r} = \mathbf{a}_2 + \mathbf{b}_2 + \mathbf{c}_2,$$

then

$$\mathbf{a}_1 - \mathbf{a}_2 = (\mathbf{b}_2 - \mathbf{b}_1) + (\mathbf{c}_2 - \mathbf{c}_1).$$

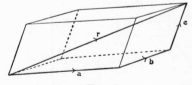

FIG. 3

Now $\mathbf{b}_2 - \mathbf{b}_1$ is in one of the given directions and $\mathbf{c}_2 - \mathbf{c}_1$ is in another, so the sum of these two vectors is a vector in the plane of these two directions. This cannot be in the direction of $\mathbf{a}_1 - \mathbf{a}_2$, which is in the third direction unless $\mathbf{a}_1 = \mathbf{a}_2$. Similarly it may be shown that $\mathbf{b}_1 = \mathbf{b}_2$ and $\mathbf{c}_1 = \mathbf{c}_2$. Thus the resolution is unique.

A similar argument will show that any vector lying in a plane may be uniquely resolved into two components in *any* two given directions which are parallel to the plane.

We choose rectangular axes $OXYZ$. Let $\mathbf{i}, \mathbf{j}, \mathbf{k}$ be three vectors of unit length in the directions $\overline{OX}, \overline{OY}, \overline{OZ}$ respectively. Now $x\mathbf{i}$ is a vector of length x in the $\overline{OX}$ direction, $y\mathbf{j}$ is one of length y in the $\overline{OY}$ direction and $z\mathbf{k}$ is one of length z in the $\overline{OZ}$ direction, so if P be the point (x, y, z) and $\mathbf{r}$ is represented by $\overline{OP}$, then (fig. 4)

$$\mathbf{r} = x\mathbf{i} + y\mathbf{j} + z\mathbf{k}.$$

Evidently $x = r \cos \alpha$, $y = r \cos \beta$, $z = r \cos \gamma$, where $\alpha = X\hat{O}P$, $\beta = Y\hat{O}P$, $\gamma = Z\hat{O}P$. $\cos \alpha$, $\cos \beta$, $\cos \gamma$ are called the **direction cosines** of the line $\overline{OP}$ or of any line in the direction

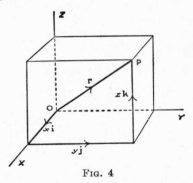

Fig. 4

of $O\overline{P}$. The direction cosines may be denoted by λ, μ, ν. It is usual to denote the components of $\mathbf{a}$ in the three coordinate directions by $a_x\mathbf{i}$, $a_y\mathbf{j}$, $a_z\mathbf{k}$. Thus

$$\mathbf{a} = a_x\mathbf{i} + a_y\mathbf{j} + a_z\mathbf{k}.$$

§ 2. We define the **scalar product** * of two vectors **a** and **b** as $ab \cos \theta$ where θ is the angle between the directions of the two vectors. We write

$$\mathbf{a} \cdot \mathbf{b} = ab \cos \theta = \mathbf{b} \cdot \mathbf{a}. \quad . \quad . \quad . \quad (1)$$

We notice that the scalar product of two vectors is not a vector but a scalar, and that scalar multiplication is commutative. If two vectors are perpendicular, their scalar product is zero since $\cos \theta = 0$. In particular

$$\mathbf{i} \cdot \mathbf{j} = \mathbf{j} \cdot \mathbf{k} = \mathbf{k} \cdot \mathbf{i} = 0. \quad . \quad . \quad . \quad (2)$$

If **a** and **b** have the same direction, $\mathbf{a} \cdot \mathbf{b} = ab$. In particular

$$\mathbf{i} \cdot \mathbf{i} = \mathbf{j} \cdot \mathbf{j} = \mathbf{k} \cdot \mathbf{k} = 1. \quad . \quad . \quad . \quad (3)$$

Since $\mathbf{a} \cdot \mathbf{b}$ is the length of **a** multiplied by the projected length of **b** on **a**, it follows that

$$\mathbf{a} \cdot (\mathbf{b} + \mathbf{c}) = \mathbf{a} \cdot \mathbf{b} + \mathbf{a} \cdot \mathbf{c},$$

for the projection of $\mathbf{b} + \mathbf{c}$ on **a** is the sum of the projections of **b** and **c** on **a**. Evidently

$$m(\mathbf{a} \cdot \mathbf{b}) = (m\mathbf{a}) \cdot \mathbf{b} = \mathbf{a} \cdot (m\mathbf{b}).$$

From these results we see that if

$$\mathbf{a} = a_x \mathbf{i} + a_y \mathbf{j} + a_z \mathbf{k}, \quad \mathbf{b} = b_x \mathbf{i} + b_y \mathbf{j} + b_z \mathbf{k},$$

then

$$
\begin{aligned}
\mathbf{a} \cdot \mathbf{b} &= (a_x \mathbf{i} + a_y \mathbf{j} + a_z \mathbf{k}) \cdot (b_x \mathbf{i} + b_y \mathbf{j} + b_z \mathbf{k}) \\
&= a_x b_x \mathbf{i} \cdot \mathbf{i} + a_x b_y \mathbf{i} \cdot \mathbf{j} + a_x b_z \mathbf{i} \cdot \mathbf{k} + a_y b_x \mathbf{j} \cdot \mathbf{i} + a_y b_y \mathbf{j} \cdot \mathbf{j} \\
&\quad + a_y b_z \mathbf{j} \cdot \mathbf{k} + a_z b_x \mathbf{k} \cdot \mathbf{i} + a_z b_y \mathbf{k} \cdot \mathbf{j} + a_z b_z \mathbf{k} \cdot \mathbf{k},
\end{aligned}
$$

or

$$\mathbf{a} \cdot \mathbf{b} = a_x b_x + a_y b_y + a_z b_z. \quad . \quad . \quad . \quad (4)$$

Hence

$$\cos \theta = (a_x b_x + a_y b_y + a_z b_z)/ab = \lambda_a \lambda_b + \mu_a \mu_b + \nu_a \nu_b, \quad (5)$$

where $(\lambda_a \mu_a \nu_a)$ and $(\lambda_b \mu_b \nu_b)$ are the direction cosines of

* See footnote † on p. 6.

a and **b** respectively, for $\lambda_a = a_x/a$, $\mu_a = a_y/a$, $\nu_a = a_z/a$, and similarly for λ_b, μ_b, ν_b.

a . a denotes the square of the length of **a** and is sometimes written as $\mathbf{a}^2$. $a^2 = a^2 = a_x{}^2 + a_y{}^2 + a_z{}^2$

§3. A rotation may be represented in magnitude and direction by a line whose length is proportional to the angle through which the rotation is made and whose direction is that of the axis of rotation.* We must, however, adopt a convention as to how we represent rotations about the same axis in opposite directions. We adopt a right-handed system of coordinate axes and represent a positive rotation through an angle $\pi/2$ from OX to OY by a line in the same direction as $\overline{OZ}$. A rotation from OY to OX would therefore be represented by a line in the direction of $\overline{ZO}$ (fig. 5).

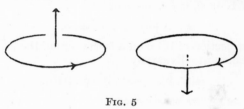

FIG. 5

The **vector product** of two vectors **a** and **b** is the vector $ab \sin \theta \, \mathbf{c}$, where θ is the angle between the directions of the two vectors and **c** is a vector of unit length perpendicular to both **a** and **b** and in the same direction as the line which represents a rotation from **a** to **b**. We denote the vector product † of **a** and **b** by $\mathbf{a} \times \mathbf{b}$. It follows from definition that

$$\mathbf{a} \times \mathbf{b} = -\mathbf{b} \times \mathbf{a}. \qquad . \qquad . \qquad . \qquad (6)$$

* Finite rotations cannot be added like distances and so should not be regarded as vectors.

† Various conventions are employed by other writers to denote scalar and vector products. Among these may be mentioned the use of (**ab**) to denote the scalar product and [**ab**] or $\mathbf{a} \wedge \mathbf{b}$ to denote the vector product.

If **a** and **b** are parallel, then $\mathbf{a} \times \mathbf{b} = 0$ since $\sin \theta = 0$. In particular $\mathbf{a} \times \mathbf{a} = 0$ and

$$\mathbf{i} \times \mathbf{i} = \mathbf{j} \times \mathbf{j} = \mathbf{k} \times \mathbf{k} = 0. \quad . \quad . \quad . \quad (7)$$

Also from definition *since i, j, k are unit vectors.*

$$\mathbf{i} \times \mathbf{j} = \mathbf{k} = -\mathbf{j} \times \mathbf{i}, \quad \mathbf{j} \times \mathbf{k} = \mathbf{i} = -\mathbf{k} \times \mathbf{j}, \quad \mathbf{k} \times \mathbf{i} = \mathbf{j} = -\mathbf{i} \times \mathbf{k}. \quad (8)$$

It may further be shown that

$$\mathbf{a} \times (\mathbf{b} + \mathbf{c}) = \mathbf{a} \times \mathbf{b} + \mathbf{a} \times \mathbf{c};$$

for, let **b′**, **c′** be the projections of **b**, **c** on the plane perpendicular to **a**. Then **b′** + **c′** is the projection of **b** + **c** on this plane. Evidently

$$\mathbf{a} \times \mathbf{b}' = \mathbf{a} \times \mathbf{b}, \quad \mathbf{a} \times \mathbf{c}' = \mathbf{a} \times \mathbf{c}, \quad \mathbf{a} \times (\mathbf{b}' + \mathbf{c}') = \mathbf{a} \times (\mathbf{b} + \mathbf{c}).$$

But since **a** is perpendicular to **b′** and **c′**, **a** × **b′** lies in the plane perpendicular to **a**, is of a times the length of **b′** and is perpendicular to **b′**; also **a** × **c′** is in this plane, is of a times the length of **c′** and is perpendicular to **c′**. It follows that **a** × **b′** + **a** × **c′** lies in this plane, is of a times the length of **b′** + **c′** and is perpendicular to **b′** + **c′**. In other words

$$\mathbf{a} \times \mathbf{b}' + \mathbf{a} \times \mathbf{c}' = \mathbf{a} \times (\mathbf{b}' + \mathbf{c}'),$$

whence we obtain the required result.

It follows from the preceding that

$$\begin{aligned}
\mathbf{a} \times \mathbf{b} &= (a_x\mathbf{i} + a_y\mathbf{j} + a_z\mathbf{k}) \times (b_x\mathbf{i} + b_y\mathbf{j} + b_z\mathbf{k}) \\
&= (a_yb_z - a_zb_y)\mathbf{i} + (a_zb_x - a_xb_z)\mathbf{j} + (a_xb_y - a_yb_x)\mathbf{k} \\
&= \begin{vmatrix} a_x & a_y & a_z \\ b_x & b_y & b_z \\ \mathbf{i} & \mathbf{j} & \mathbf{k} \end{vmatrix} \quad . \quad . \quad . \quad . \quad . \quad . \quad (9)
\end{aligned}$$

Some writers define the vector product by equation (9) and deduce its other properties from this formula.

$$= a_x b_x \, \underline{i} \times \underline{i} + a_x b_y \, \underline{i \cdot j} + a_x b_z \, \underline{i} \times \underline{k} + a_y b_x \, \underline{j} \times \underline{i}$$
$$+ a_y b_y \, \underline{j \times j} + a_y b_z \, \underline{j \times k} + a_z b_x \, \underline{k \cdot} \times \underline{i} + a_z b_y \, \underline{k \cdot j}$$
$$+ a_z b_z \, \underline{k \times k} =$$

§ 4. If **a**, **b** and **c** be three arbitrary vectors, then the scalar product of **a** × **b** with **c** is called the **triple scalar product** of **a**, **b** and **c**, and is written [**a**, **b**, **c**].

$$\mathbf{a} \times \mathbf{b} \cdot \mathbf{c} = (a_y b_z - a_z b_y)c_x + (a_z b_x - a_x b_z)c_y + (a_x b_y - a_y b_x)c_z,$$

so $[\mathbf{a}, \mathbf{b}, \mathbf{c}] = \begin{vmatrix} a_x & a_y & a_z \\ b_x & b_y & b_z \\ c_x & c_y & c_z \end{vmatrix}$.   .   .   (10)

It follows from (1) and (6) that

$$[\mathbf{a}, \mathbf{b}, \mathbf{c}] = [\mathbf{b}, \mathbf{c}, \mathbf{a}] = [\mathbf{c}, \mathbf{a}, \mathbf{b}]$$
$$= -[\mathbf{a}, \mathbf{c}, \mathbf{b}] = -[\mathbf{b}, \mathbf{a}, \mathbf{c}] = -[\mathbf{c}, \mathbf{b}, \mathbf{a}].$$

From fig. 6 we see that [**a**, **b**, **c**] represents the volume of the parallelepiped which has **a**, **b** and **c** for concurrent sides.

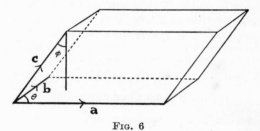

FIG. 6

For **a** × **b** = $ab \sin \theta$ **p**, where **p** is a unit vector perpendicular to **a** and **b**,   So

$$[\mathbf{a}, \mathbf{b}, \mathbf{c}] = ab \sin \theta \ \mathbf{p} \cdot \mathbf{c} = ab \sin \theta \ c \cos \phi$$
$$= area \ of \ base \times perpendicular \ height.$$

If [**a**, **b**, **c**] = 0, the volume of the parallelepiped is zero. Hence the condition that **a**, **b** and **c** be coplanar is [**a**, **b**, **c**] = 0. We observe in particular that if any two of the vectors **a**, **b**, **c** be equal, then [**a**, **b**, **c**] ≡ 0.

§ 5. We can evaluate the **triple vector product** $\mathbf{a} \times (\mathbf{b} \times \mathbf{c})$ by using the formula (9) twice over. We find that

$$\mathbf{a} \times (\mathbf{b} \times \mathbf{c}) = \{a_y(b_x c_y - b_y c_x) - a_z(b_z c_x - b_x c_z)\}\mathbf{i}$$
$$+ \{a_z(b_y c_z - b_z c_y) - a_x(b_x c_y - b_y c_x)\}\mathbf{j}$$
$$+ \{a_x(b_z c_x - b_x c_z) - a_y(b_y c_z - b_z c_y)\}\mathbf{k}$$
$$= (a_x c_x + a_y c_y + a_z c_z)(b_x\mathbf{i} + b_y\mathbf{j} + b_z\mathbf{k})$$
$$- (a_x b_x + a_y b_y + a_z b_z)(c_x\mathbf{i} + c_y\mathbf{j} + c_z\mathbf{k}).$$

So
$$\mathbf{a} \times (\mathbf{b} \times \mathbf{c}) = (\mathbf{a} \cdot \mathbf{c})\mathbf{b} - (\mathbf{a} \cdot \mathbf{b})\mathbf{c}. \quad . \quad (11)$$

The order of vector multiplication must be shown by brackets for, as is easily verified,

$$\mathbf{a} \times (\mathbf{b} \times \mathbf{c}) \neq (\mathbf{a} \times \mathbf{b}) \times \mathbf{c}.$$

We obtain the identity

$$\mathbf{a} \times (\mathbf{b} \times \mathbf{c}) + \mathbf{b} \times (\mathbf{c} \times \mathbf{a}) + \mathbf{c} \times (\mathbf{a} \times \mathbf{b}) \equiv \mathbf{0}, \quad \bullet \quad (12)$$

for by (11) the left-hand side is

$$(\mathbf{a} \cdot \mathbf{c})\mathbf{b} - (\mathbf{a} \cdot \mathbf{b})\mathbf{c} + (\mathbf{b} \cdot \mathbf{a})\mathbf{c} - (\mathbf{b} \cdot \mathbf{c})\mathbf{a} + (\mathbf{c} \cdot \mathbf{b})\mathbf{a} - (\mathbf{c} \cdot \mathbf{a})\mathbf{b},$$

which vanishes identically.

§ 6. For purposes of reference we shall evaluate **two** other products each involving four vectors.

$$(\mathbf{a} \times \mathbf{b}) \cdot (\mathbf{c} \times \mathbf{d}) = [\mathbf{a}, \mathbf{b}, \mathbf{c} \times \mathbf{d}] = [\mathbf{b}, \mathbf{c} \times \mathbf{d}, \mathbf{a}]$$
$$= \mathbf{b} \times (\mathbf{c} \times \mathbf{d}) \cdot \mathbf{a} = \{(\mathbf{b} \cdot \mathbf{d})\mathbf{c} - (\mathbf{b} \cdot \mathbf{c})\mathbf{d}\} \cdot \mathbf{a}$$
$$= (\mathbf{b} \cdot \mathbf{d})(\mathbf{c} \cdot \mathbf{a}) - (\mathbf{b} \cdot \mathbf{c})(\mathbf{d} \cdot \mathbf{a}). \quad . \quad (13)$$

In particular

$$(\mathbf{a} \times \mathbf{b})^2 = \mathbf{b}^2\mathbf{a}^2 - (\mathbf{a} \cdot \mathbf{b})^2, \quad . \quad . \quad (14)$$

which merely states that $a^2 b^2 \sin^2 \theta = a^2 b^2 - a^2 b^2 \cos^2 \theta$.

Again from (11)

$$(\mathbf{a} \times \mathbf{b}) \times (\mathbf{c} \times \mathbf{d}) = (\mathbf{a} \times \mathbf{b} \cdot \mathbf{d})\mathbf{c} - (\mathbf{a} \times \mathbf{b} \cdot \mathbf{c})\mathbf{d}$$
$$= [\mathbf{a}, \mathbf{b}, \mathbf{d}]\mathbf{c} - [\mathbf{a}, \mathbf{b}, \mathbf{c}]\mathbf{d} \quad \bullet \quad (15)$$
$$= (\mathbf{c} \times \mathbf{d}) \times (\mathbf{b} \times \mathbf{a}) = [\mathbf{c}, \mathbf{d}, \mathbf{a}]\mathbf{b} - [\mathbf{c}, \mathbf{d}, \mathbf{b}]\mathbf{a}.$$

So we have the identity

$$[\mathbf{a},\, \mathbf{b},\, \mathbf{c}]\mathbf{d} \equiv [\mathbf{d},\, \mathbf{b},\, \mathbf{c}]\mathbf{a} + [\mathbf{a},\, \mathbf{d},\, \mathbf{c}]\mathbf{b} + [\mathbf{a},\, \mathbf{b},\, \mathbf{d}]\mathbf{c}, \quad (16)$$

showing how any vector $\mathbf{d}$ may be expressed as a linear combination of any three given non-coplanar vectors $\mathbf{a}, \mathbf{b}, \mathbf{c}$.

§ 7. We may have variable vectors with variable components along the coordinate axes. Let $\mathbf{a} = a_x\mathbf{i} + a_y\mathbf{j} + a_z\mathbf{k}$ be a variable vector, then $\delta\mathbf{a} = (\delta a_x)\mathbf{i} + (\delta a_y)\mathbf{j} + (\delta a_z)\mathbf{k}$. If a_x, a_y, a_z be functions of a variable t, then

$$\frac{d\mathbf{a}}{dt} = \frac{da_x}{dt}\mathbf{i} + \frac{da_y}{dt}\mathbf{j} + \frac{da_z}{dt}\mathbf{k}$$

is also a vector. In like manner

$$\frac{d}{dt}(\mathbf{a} \cdot \mathbf{b}) = \frac{d}{dt}(a_x b_x + a_y b_y + a_z b_z)$$

$$= a_x\frac{db_x}{dt} + a_y\frac{db_y}{dt} + a_z\frac{db_z}{dt} + b_x\frac{da_x}{dt} + b_y\frac{da_y}{dt} + b_z\frac{da_z}{dt}$$

$$= \left(\mathbf{a} \cdot \frac{d\mathbf{b}}{dt}\right) + \left(\frac{d\mathbf{a}}{dt} \cdot \mathbf{b}\right);$$

and

$$\frac{d}{dt}(\mathbf{a} \times \mathbf{b})$$

$$= \left(a_y\frac{db_z}{dt} - a_z\frac{db_y}{dt}\right)\mathbf{i} + \left(a_z\frac{db_x}{dt} - a_x\frac{db_z}{dt}\right)\mathbf{j} + \left(a_x\frac{db_y}{dt} - a_y\frac{db_x}{dt}\right)\mathbf{k}$$

$$+ \left(\frac{da_y}{dt}b_z - \frac{da_z}{dt}b_y\right)\mathbf{i} + \left(\frac{da_z}{dt}b_x - \frac{da_x}{dt}b_z\right)\mathbf{j} + \left(\frac{da_x}{dt}b_y - \frac{da_y}{dt}b_x\right)\mathbf{k}$$

$$= \left(\mathbf{a} \times \frac{d\mathbf{b}}{dt}\right) + \left(\frac{d\mathbf{a}}{dt} \times \mathbf{b}\right).$$

§ 8. **Examples**

(1) Prove that if $a\overline{OP} + \beta\overline{OQ} + \gamma\overline{OR} + \delta\overline{OS} = 0$ and $a + \beta + \gamma + \delta = 0$ where a, β, γ, δ are not all zero, then P, Q, R, S are co-planar.

(2) ABC, $A'B'C'$ are two triangles and G, G' are their centroids. Prove that $\overline{AA'} + \overline{BB'} + \overline{CC'} = 3\overline{GG'}$.

(3) Evaluate $(\mathbf{a} + \mathbf{b}) \cdot (\mathbf{a} - \mathbf{b})$ in the case where $a = b$ and interpret geometrically.

(4) $\mathbf{t}$, $\mathbf{n}$, $\mathbf{b}$ are three mutually perpendicular unit vectors and their components are all functions of a single scalar variable. Show that $\mathbf{t'}$, $\mathbf{n'}$, $\mathbf{b'}$ are coplanar, where the dash denotes differentiation.

(5) Prove that $\mathbf{a} \times (\mathbf{b} \times \mathbf{c}) = (\mathbf{a} \cdot \mathbf{c})\mathbf{b} - (\mathbf{a} \cdot \mathbf{b})\mathbf{c}$ by a method which does not involve the resolution of the vectors into components. [Prove first for the case $\mathbf{a} = \mathbf{b}$.]

(6) If $\mathbf{a} + \mathbf{b} + \mathbf{c} = 0$, prove that $\mathbf{a} \times \mathbf{b} = \mathbf{b} \times \mathbf{c} = \mathbf{c} \times \mathbf{a}$, and interpret geometrically.

(7) Four vectors are proportional to the areas of the four faces of a tetrahedron and their directions are the outward perpendiculars from the respective faces. Show that the sum of these four vectors is the zero vector.

(8) Show that $[\mathbf{a} \times \mathbf{b}, \mathbf{a} \times \mathbf{c}, \mathbf{d}] = (\mathbf{a} \cdot \mathbf{d})[\mathbf{a}, \mathbf{b}, \mathbf{c}]$.

APPLICATIONS TO ELEMENTARY GEOMETRY

§ 9. The **position vector** of a point P is the vector drawn from the origin O to P. If P is a variable point we denote the variable position vector by

$$\mathbf{r} = x\mathbf{i} + y\mathbf{j} + z\mathbf{k},$$

(x, y, z) being the coordinates of the point P. Let $\mathbf{r}_0$ be the position vector of any fixed point on the line whose direction is that of the unit vector $\mathbf{t}$ with direction cosines λ, μ, ν. The position vector of any other point on this line is then of the form

$$\mathbf{r} = \mathbf{r}_0 + k\mathbf{t}. \qquad . \qquad . \qquad . \qquad . \qquad (17)$$

As k takes different values, $\mathbf{r}$ determines different points on this line. (17) is the vector equation to the straight line and represents three scalar equations

$$x = x_0 + k\lambda, \quad y = y_0 + k\mu, \quad z = z_0 + k\nu,$$

which give the well-known equation to a straight line

$$\frac{x - x_0}{\lambda} = \frac{y - y_0}{\mu} = \frac{z - z_0}{\nu}. \qquad \cdot \qquad \cdot \qquad \cdot \qquad (18)$$

In the same way, if h and k are variable scalars, then

$$\boxed{\mathbf{r} = \mathbf{r}_0 + h\mathbf{s} + k\mathbf{t}} \qquad \cdot \qquad \cdot \qquad \cdot \qquad (19)$$

is the vector equation to the plane through the point $\mathbf{r}_0$ which contains the directions of both $\mathbf{s}$ and $\mathbf{t}$. The three scalar equations are

$$x = x_0 + hs_x + kt_x, \quad y = y_0 + hs_y + kt_y, \quad z = z_0 + hs_z + kt_z.$$

On eliminating the parameters h and k from these, we get

$$\begin{vmatrix} (x - x_0) & (y - y_0) & (z - z_0) \\ s_x & s_y & s_z \\ t_x & t_y & t_z \end{vmatrix} = 0$$

or $\qquad\qquad \boxed{(\mathbf{r} - \mathbf{r}_0) \cdot (\mathbf{s} \times \mathbf{t}) = 0} \qquad \cdot \qquad \cdot \qquad \cdot \qquad (20)$

as the equation of the plane. $\mathbf{s} \times \mathbf{t}$ is in a direction perpendicular to the plane, so its components are proportional to the direction cosines (λ, μ, ν) of the normal to the plane. The equation to the plane may therefore be written as

$$\lambda(x - x_0) + \mu(y - y_0) + \nu(z - z_0) = 0. \qquad \cdot \qquad \cdot \qquad (21)$$

Examples § 10. *To show that the medians of a triangle are concurrent.*
Let the triangle be OAB and choose O as the origin. Let $\overline{OA}$ be $\mathbf{a}$ and let $\overline{OB}$ be $\mathbf{b}$. Let OD, AE, BF be the medians and let AE and BF meet in G. Now $\overline{AB} = \mathbf{b} - \mathbf{a}$, so $\overline{AD} = \frac{1}{2}(\mathbf{b} - \mathbf{a})$; hence $\overline{OD} = \overline{OA} + \overline{AD} = \mathbf{a} + \frac{1}{2}(\mathbf{b} - \mathbf{a})$ $= \frac{1}{2}(\mathbf{a} + \mathbf{b})$. Further, $\overline{OE} = \frac{1}{2}\mathbf{b}$, so $\overline{EA} = \mathbf{a} - \frac{1}{2}\mathbf{b}$ and the equation to the line EA is $\mathbf{r} = \frac{1}{2}\mathbf{b} + k(\mathbf{a} - \frac{1}{2}\mathbf{b})$. Hence $\overline{OG} = k\mathbf{a} + \frac{1}{2}(1 - k)\mathbf{b}$ for some value of k to be determined. Similarly $\overline{OG} = h\mathbf{b} + \frac{1}{2}(1 - h)\mathbf{a}$ for some value of h. But these two resolutions of $\overline{OG}$ into components in the directions of

a and **b** must be identical, so $k = \frac{1}{2}(1-h)$ and $h = \frac{1}{2}(1-k)$, whence $h = k = \frac{1}{3}$ and $\overline{OG} = \frac{1}{3}(\mathbf{a}+\mathbf{b})$. I.e., $\overline{OG} = \frac{2}{3}\overline{OD}$, which means that OG will pass through D and that $OG = \frac{2}{3}OD$.

§ **11.** *To show that the lines joining the mid-points of the opposite edges of a tetrahedron* OABC *are concurrent and bisect one another.*

Choose O as the origin. Let D, E, F be the mid-points of OA, OB, OC and let K, L, M be the mid-points of AB, BC, CA. Let $\overline{OA} = \mathbf{a}, \overline{OB} = \mathbf{b}, \overline{OC} = \mathbf{c}$, then $\overline{AB} = \mathbf{b} - \mathbf{a}$, $\overline{BC} = \mathbf{c} - \mathbf{b}$, $\overline{CA} = \mathbf{a} - \mathbf{c}$. Also $\overline{OD} = \frac{1}{2}\mathbf{a}$ and $\overline{OL} = \frac{1}{2}(\mathbf{b}+\mathbf{c})$, so if W is the mid-point of DL we have $\overline{OW} = \frac{1}{4}(\mathbf{a}+\mathbf{b}+\mathbf{c})$. By the symmetry of this result it is evident that W lies on and bisects both EM and FK, which proves the theorem.

§ **12.** *To prove that the altitudes of a triangle are concurrent.*

Let the triangle be ABC and let the altitudes through B and C intersect in O. Let $\overline{OA} = \mathbf{a}, \overline{OB} = \mathbf{b}$ and $\overline{OC} = \mathbf{c}$, then $\overline{AB} = \mathbf{b} - \mathbf{a}$, $\overline{BC} = \mathbf{c} - \mathbf{b}$ and $\overline{CA} = \mathbf{a} - \mathbf{c}$. Since OB and CA are perpendicular we have

$$\mathbf{b} \cdot (\mathbf{a}-\mathbf{c}) = 0 \quad \text{or} \quad \mathbf{b} \cdot \mathbf{a} = \mathbf{b} \cdot \mathbf{c};$$

and since OC and AB are perpendicular

$$\mathbf{c} \cdot (\mathbf{b}-\mathbf{a}) = 0 \quad \text{or} \quad \mathbf{c} \cdot \mathbf{b} = \mathbf{c} \cdot \mathbf{a}.$$

Hence $\qquad \mathbf{a} \cdot (\mathbf{c}-\mathbf{b}) = \mathbf{a} \cdot \mathbf{c} - \mathbf{a} \cdot \mathbf{b} = 0,$

showing that OA and BC are perpendicular. This proves the theorem.

§ **13. The Orthocentric Tetrahedron.*** A tetrahedron does not in general possess an orthocentre, but it may do so, and we shall consider a tetrahedron $ABCD$ with an orthocentre O. Suppose that the altitudes from A, B, C, D meet the opposite faces in H, K, L, M respect-

* H. Lob., *Math. Gazette*, xix. (1935), p. 102.

ively. Let $\overline{OA} = \mathbf{a}$, $\overline{OB} = \mathbf{b}$, $\overline{OC} = \mathbf{c}$, $\overline{OD} = \mathbf{d}$, then $\overline{BC} = \mathbf{c} - \mathbf{b}$ and $\overline{CD} = \mathbf{d} - \mathbf{c}$. Since OA is perpendicular to the plane BCD, we must have $\mathbf{a} \cdot (\mathbf{c} - \mathbf{b}) = 0$ and $\mathbf{a} \cdot (\mathbf{d} - \mathbf{c}) = 0$.

So
$$\left. \begin{aligned} \mathbf{a} \cdot \mathbf{b} &= \mathbf{a} \cdot \mathbf{c} = \mathbf{a} \cdot \mathbf{d}. \\ \text{Similarly} \quad \mathbf{b} \cdot \mathbf{a} &= \mathbf{b} \cdot \mathbf{c} = \mathbf{b} \cdot \mathbf{d}, \\ \text{and} \quad \mathbf{c} \cdot \mathbf{a} &= \mathbf{c} \cdot \mathbf{b} = \mathbf{c} \cdot \mathbf{d}. \end{aligned} \right\} \qquad . \qquad . \qquad (22)$$

So all the scalar products are equal ($= \sigma$ say). In other words

$$(OA)(OH) = (OB)(OK) = (OC)(OL) = (OD)(OM) = \sigma.$$

Two edges which do not meet are perpendicular, e.g.,

$$(\mathbf{b} - \mathbf{a}) \cdot (\mathbf{d} - \mathbf{c}) = \mathbf{b} \cdot \mathbf{d} - \mathbf{b} \cdot \mathbf{c} - \mathbf{a} \cdot \mathbf{d} + \mathbf{a} \cdot \mathbf{c}$$
$$= \sigma - \sigma - \sigma + \sigma = 0.$$

so AB is perpendicular to CD.

Again BH is in the plane OAB so $\overline{BH} = h\mathbf{a} + k\mathbf{b}$ where h, k have certain values. Thus

$$(h\mathbf{a} + k\mathbf{b}) \cdot (\mathbf{d} - \mathbf{c}) = h\sigma - h\sigma + k\sigma - k\sigma = 0,$$

i.e., BH is perpendicular to CD. In other words, the feet of the altitudes are the orthocentres of the faces.

Let Q be the circumcentre and let R be the radius of the circumsphere. If $\overline{OQ} = \mathbf{q}$, then

$$(\mathbf{q} - \mathbf{a}) \cdot (\mathbf{q} - \mathbf{a}) = R^2 = (\mathbf{q} - \mathbf{b}) \cdot (\mathbf{q} - \mathbf{b}),$$

whence $2\mathbf{q} \cdot (\mathbf{a} - \mathbf{b}) = a^2 - b^2.$

Similarly $2\mathbf{q} \cdot (\mathbf{a} - \mathbf{c}) = a^2 - c^2,$

. . . .

From (22) we see that $\mathbf{q} = \frac{1}{2}(\mathbf{a} + \mathbf{b} + \mathbf{c} + \mathbf{d})$ satisfies all these equations. If G be the centroid of the vertices, then $\overline{OG} = \frac{1}{4}(\mathbf{a} + \mathbf{b} + \mathbf{c} + \mathbf{d})$, so G bisects OQ. Further

$$R^2 = \frac{1}{2}(-\mathbf{a} + \mathbf{b} + \mathbf{c} + \mathbf{d}) \cdot \frac{1}{2}(-\mathbf{a} + \mathbf{b} + \mathbf{c} + \mathbf{d})$$
$$= \frac{1}{4}(a^2 + b^2 + c^2 + d^2 - 6\sigma + 6\sigma)$$
$$= \frac{1}{4}(a^2 + b^2 + c^2 + d^2).$$

§ **14.**   Examples

(1) *ABCD* is a parallelogram and *E* is the mid-point of *AB*. Prove that *DE* and *AC* trisect one another.

(2) Prove Desargues' theorem by vector methods.

(3) Prove that the perpendicular bisectors of the sides of a triangle are concurrent.

(4) The position vectors of the foci of an ellipse are **c** and – **c** and the length of the major axis is $2a$. Show that the equation to the ellipse may be written

$$a^4 - a^2(\mathbf{r}^2 + \mathbf{c}^2) + (\mathbf{c}\,.\,\mathbf{r})^2 = 0.$$

(5) Show that the equation to the perpendicular from the point **b** to the line $\mathbf{r} = \mathbf{a} + k\mathbf{t}$ is

$$\mathbf{r} = \mathbf{b} + h\mathbf{t} \times \{(\mathbf{a} - \mathbf{b}) \times \mathbf{t}\}.$$

(6) Show that the two straight lines $\mathbf{r} = \mathbf{a} + k\mathbf{u}$ and $\mathbf{r} = \mathbf{b} + h\mathbf{v}$ intersect if $[\mathbf{v}, \mathbf{b}, \mathbf{u}] = [\mathbf{v}, \mathbf{a}, \mathbf{u}]$ and that the point of intersection is

$$\mathbf{a} + \frac{[\mathbf{a}, \mathbf{b}, \mathbf{v}]}{[\mathbf{v}, \mathbf{a}, \mathbf{u}]}\mathbf{u} \quad \text{or} \quad \mathbf{b} + \frac{[\mathbf{a}, \mathbf{b}, \mathbf{u}]}{[\mathbf{v}, \mathbf{b}, \mathbf{u}]}\mathbf{v}.$$

(7) *ABCD* is a tetrahedron and *O* is any point. *AO*, *BO*, *CO*, *DO* meet the opposite faces in *E*, *F*, *G*, *H* respectively. Prove that

$$\overline{AO}/\overline{AE} + \overline{BO}/\overline{BF} + \overline{CO}/\overline{CG} + \overline{DO}/\overline{DH} = 3.$$

(8) Prove Ceva's theorem by vector methods.

(9) Prove Menelaus's theorem by vector methods.

(10) Prove that triangles with equal areas on the same base and on the same side of it lie between the same parallels.

(11) Show that the plane through the points $\mathbf{r}_1$, $\mathbf{r}_2$, $\mathbf{r}_3$ has the equation

$$[\mathbf{r}, \mathbf{r}_2, \mathbf{r}_3] + [\mathbf{r}, \mathbf{r}_3, \mathbf{r}_1] + [\mathbf{r}, \mathbf{r}_1, \mathbf{r}_2] = [\mathbf{r}_1, \mathbf{r}_2, \mathbf{r}_3].$$

CHAPTER II

DIFFERENTIAL GEOMETRY

TWISTED CURVES

§ 15. THE parametric equations of a curve in three-dimensional space may be written

$$x = x(u), \quad y = y(u), \quad z = z(u), \qquad . \qquad . \qquad (1)$$

where u is a variable parameter and x, y, z are rectangular Cartesian coordinates. If we eliminate u from the equations (1), we get two equations, say

$$\phi_1(x, y, z) = 0, \quad \phi_2(x, y, z) = 0$$

representing two surfaces, all or part of whose intersection is the curve (1).

If dl be the element of length, then

$$dl^2 = dx^2 + dy^2 + dz^2 = \left\{ \left(\frac{dx}{du}\right)^2 + \left(\frac{dy}{du}\right)^2 + \left(\frac{dz}{du}\right)^2 \right\} du^2. \qquad (2)$$

The length of the arc measured along the curve from some given point u_0 to an arbitrary point u is

$$l = \int_0^l dl = \int_{u_0}^{u} \left\{ \left(\frac{dx}{du}\right)^2 + \left(\frac{dy}{du}\right)^2 + \left(\frac{dz}{du}\right)^2 \right\}^{\frac{1}{2}} du. \qquad (3)$$

This equation expresses l as a function of u. If we can solve the above equation for u in terms of l and obtain say $u = F(l)$, then substituting in (1) we have the equation of the curve in the form

$$x = x(l), \quad y = y(l), \quad z = z(l).$$

From (2) the necessary and sufficient condition that the

16

parameter u be the arc l measured from some point on the curve is

$$\left(\frac{dx}{du}\right)^2 + \left(\frac{dy}{du}\right)^2 + \left(\frac{dz}{du}\right)^2 = 1. \qquad . \qquad . \qquad (4)$$

Let $\mathbf{r} = x\mathbf{i} + y\mathbf{j} + z\mathbf{k}$ be the position vector of any point on the curve. We write $\mathbf{r} = \mathbf{r}(l)$ to denote that the co-ordinates x, y, z are each functions of the parameter l. Using a dash to denote differentiation with respect to l, we see that the components x', y', z' of $\mathbf{r}'$ are precisely the direction cosines of the tangent to the curve at the point $\mathbf{r}$. Also, $\mathbf{r}'$ is of unit length, since $(x')^2 + (y')^2 + (z')^2 = 1$. We call $\mathbf{r}'$ the **unit tangent**. The equation of the tangent to the curve at the point $\mathbf{r}_1$ is therefore

$$\mathbf{r} = \mathbf{r}_1 + k\mathbf{r}'_1,$$

where k is a variable scalar.

On differentiating the relation $\mathbf{r}' . \mathbf{r}' = 1$, we have

$$\mathbf{r}' . \mathbf{r}'' = 0,$$

showing that $\mathbf{r}''$ is perpendicular to $\mathbf{r}'$. If the curve is a straight line, $\mathbf{r}'$ is a constant vector and therefore $\mathbf{r}'' = \mathbf{0}$ for all points on the curve. If at a point $\mathbf{r}_1$ on the curve $\mathbf{r}''_1 \neq \mathbf{0}$, then three consecutive points on the curve will determine a plane, called the **osculating plane**.

Let P, P_1, P_2 be three neighbouring points on the curve. We may take their position vectors to be

$$\overline{OP} = \mathbf{r},$$
$$\overline{OP_1} = \mathbf{r} + \mathbf{r}'\delta_1 l + \tfrac{1}{2}\mathbf{r}''(\delta_1 l)^2 + \dots,$$
$$\overline{OP_2} = \mathbf{r} + \mathbf{r}'\delta_2 l + \tfrac{1}{2}\mathbf{r}''(\delta_2 l)^2 + \dots,$$

where $\delta_1 l$ and $\delta_2 l$ are elements of length measured along the curve. It follows that

$$\overline{PP_1} = \overline{OP_1} - \overline{OP} = \mathbf{r}'\delta_1 l + \tfrac{1}{2}\mathbf{r}''(\delta_1 l)^2 + \dots,$$
$$\overline{PP_2} = \overline{OP_2} - \overline{OP} = \mathbf{r}'\delta_2 l + \tfrac{1}{2}\mathbf{r}''(\delta_2 l)^2 + \dots.$$

Now the plane PP_1P_2 must contain the vectors

$$\frac{\overline{PP_1}}{\delta_1 l} \quad \text{and} \quad \frac{2}{\delta_1 l - \delta_2 l}\left\{\frac{\overline{PP_1}}{\delta_1 l} - \frac{\overline{PP_2}}{\delta_2 l}\right\},$$

which may be written

$$\mathbf{r}' + \tfrac{1}{2}\mathbf{r}''\delta_1 l + \ldots \quad \text{and} \quad \mathbf{r}'' + \tfrac{1}{3}\mathbf{r}'''(\delta_1 l + \delta_2 l) + \ldots.$$

respectively. In the limiting case when $\delta_1 l$ and $\delta_2 l$ both tend to zero, these vectors tend to the values $\mathbf{r}'$ and $\mathbf{r}''$ respectively. At the same time P_1 and P_2 move up to and coincide with P so that the osculating plane at P is simply the limiting case of the plane PP_1P_2. From this it is evident that the osculating plane at P is parallel to the vectors $\mathbf{r}'$ and $\mathbf{r}''$ formed at P. We conclude that the equation of the osculating plane at a point whose position vector is $\mathbf{r}_1$ may be written

$$[\mathbf{r} - \mathbf{r}_1, \quad \mathbf{r}'_1, \quad \mathbf{r}''_1] = 0.$$

Evidently the normal to the osculating plane is parallel to $\mathbf{r}'_1 \times \mathbf{r}''_1$. The normal to the curve which lies in the osculating plane of the point where the normal meets the curve is called the **principal normal** at that point. Since $\mathbf{r}''_1$ is parallel to the osculating plane and is perpendicular to the tangent, its direction must be that of the principal normal. Hence the equation to the principal normal at $\mathbf{r}_1$ is

$$\mathbf{r} = \mathbf{r}_1 + k\mathbf{r}''_1,$$

where k is a variable scalar.

The direction of $\mathbf{r}'_1 \times \mathbf{r}''_1$ is perpendicular to $\mathbf{r}'_1$ and so a line drawn in this direction through $\mathbf{r}_1$ is a normal to the curve. This normal is called the **binormal**. It is perpendicular to the osculating plane and its equation is

$$\mathbf{r} = \mathbf{r}_1 + k\mathbf{r}'_1 \times \mathbf{r}''_1,$$

where k is a variable scalar.

§ **16.** Let us denote the length of $\mathbf{r}''$ by $1/\rho$, then $\rho\mathbf{r}''$ is a unit vector which we call the **unit principal normal**. Also $\mathbf{r}' \times \rho\mathbf{r}''$, or $\rho\mathbf{r}' \times \mathbf{r}''$, which is in the direction of the binormal is a unit vector, since $\mathbf{r}'$ and $\rho\mathbf{r}''$ are both unit vectors and are perpendicular to one another. $\rho\mathbf{r}' \times \mathbf{r}''$ is called the **unit binormal**. It is convenient to write $\mathbf{t}$ for $\mathbf{r}'$, $\mathbf{n}$ for $\rho\mathbf{r}''$ and $\mathbf{b}$ for $\rho\mathbf{r}' \times \mathbf{r}''$. We have now at each point of the curve three mutually perpendicular unit vectors : viz., the unit tangent $\mathbf{t}$, the unit principal normal $\mathbf{n}$ and the unit binormal $\mathbf{b}$. This configuration is called the **moving trihedral**.

We have

$$\mathbf{t}' = \mathbf{r}'' = \frac{1}{\rho}\mathbf{n}. \quad . \quad . \quad . \quad . \quad (5)$$

Now $\mathbf{b} \cdot \mathbf{b} = 1$, so $\mathbf{b} \cdot \mathbf{b}' = 0$, showing that $\mathbf{b}'$ is perpendicular to $\mathbf{b}$. Further, $\mathbf{t} \cdot \mathbf{b} = 0$, so $\mathbf{t}' \cdot \mathbf{b} + \mathbf{t} \cdot \mathbf{b}' = 0$. But the first term vanishes since $\mathbf{n} \cdot \mathbf{b} = 0$, hence $\mathbf{t} \cdot \mathbf{b}' = 0$, showing that $\mathbf{b}'$ is also perpendicular to $\mathbf{t}$. It follows that $\mathbf{b}'$ must be parallel to $\mathbf{n}$. We write

$$\mathbf{b}' = -\frac{1}{\tau}\mathbf{n}. \quad . \quad . \quad . \quad . \quad (6)$$

Now $\qquad\qquad \mathbf{n} = \mathbf{b} \times \mathbf{t},$

so $\qquad \mathbf{n}' = \mathbf{b}' \times \mathbf{t} + \mathbf{b} \times \mathbf{t}' = -\frac{1}{\tau}\mathbf{n} \times \mathbf{t} + \frac{1}{\rho}\mathbf{b} \times \mathbf{n},$

or $\qquad\qquad \mathbf{n}' = +\frac{1}{\tau}\mathbf{b} - \frac{1}{\rho}\mathbf{t}. \quad . \quad . \quad . \quad (7)$

(5), (6) and (7) are known as **Frenet's formulae**. They may be written as

$$\begin{aligned}
\mathbf{t}' &= +\frac{1}{\rho}\mathbf{n} \quad , \\
\mathbf{n}' &= -\frac{1}{\rho}\mathbf{t} +\frac{1}{\tau}\mathbf{b}, \\
\mathbf{b}' &= -\frac{1}{\tau}\mathbf{n} \quad ,
\end{aligned}$$

displaying the antisymmetric matrix. The value of $1/\rho$ at any point is called the **curvature**, and the value of $1/\tau$ is called the **torsion**.

Since
$$\mathbf{b} = \rho \mathbf{r}' \times \mathbf{r}'',$$
$$\mathbf{b}' = \rho' \mathbf{r}' \times \mathbf{r}'' + \rho \mathbf{r}'' \times \mathbf{r}'' + \rho \mathbf{r}' \times \mathbf{r}'''.$$

The middle term vanishes, so that
$$1/\tau = -\mathbf{b}' \cdot \mathbf{n}$$
$$= -(\rho' \mathbf{r}' \times \mathbf{r}'' + \rho \mathbf{r}' \times \mathbf{r}''') \cdot (\rho \mathbf{r}'')$$
$$= -\rho' \rho [\mathbf{r}', \mathbf{r}'', \mathbf{r}''] - \rho^2 [\mathbf{r}', \mathbf{r}''', \mathbf{r}''],$$

whence $1/\tau = \rho^2 [\mathbf{r}', \mathbf{r}'', \mathbf{r}''']$.   .   .   .   .   .   (8)

§ **17.** The vector equation of a sphere of radius a and centre $\mathbf{q}$ is
$$(\mathbf{r} - \mathbf{q})^2 = a^2.$$

The points where the curve $\mathbf{r} = \mathbf{r}(l)$ intersects this sphere will be obtained by solving the equation
$$f(l) \equiv (\mathbf{r}(l) - \mathbf{q})^2 - a^2 = 0$$

for l. The sphere will intersect the curve in three coincident points at $l = l_1$ if the equations
$$f(l_1) = 0, \quad f'(l_1) = 0, \quad f''(l_1) = 0$$

are simultaneously true. We wish to find the spheres which meet the curve in three coincident points at the point $\mathbf{r}$. In order that this be so a and $\mathbf{q}$ must satisfy the equations
$$(\mathbf{r} - \mathbf{q})^2 - a^2 = 0,$$
$$\mathbf{r}' \cdot (\mathbf{r} - \mathbf{q}) = 0,$$
$$\mathbf{r}'' \cdot (\mathbf{r} - \mathbf{q}) + \mathbf{r}' \cdot \mathbf{r}' = 0.$$

These may be rewritten in the form
$$(\mathbf{r} - \mathbf{q})^2 = a^2, \quad . \quad . \quad . \quad . \quad (9)$$
$$\mathbf{t} \cdot (\mathbf{r} - \mathbf{q}) = 0, \quad . \quad . \quad . \quad . \quad (10)$$
$$\mathbf{n} \cdot (\mathbf{r} - \mathbf{q}) = -\rho. \quad . \quad . \quad . \quad . \quad (11)$$

From (10), $(\mathbf{r} - \mathbf{q})$ evidently lies in the normal plane at $\mathbf{r}$, so we may suppose that $\mathbf{r} - \mathbf{q} = h\mathbf{n} + k\mathbf{b}$, where h and k are scalars which so far are undetermined. From (11), $h = -\rho$ and from (9), $k = \pm (a^2 - \rho^2)^{\frac{1}{2}}$. We see that at any point of the curve there are in general two spheres of radius a, provided a is not less than ρ, which intersect the curve at the point in question in three coincident points. The centre of such a sphere is the point

$$\mathbf{q} = \mathbf{r} + \rho\mathbf{n} \pm (a^2 - \rho^2)^{\frac{1}{2}}\mathbf{b}.$$

The radius a is still at our choice. If we choose $a = \rho$, then

$$\mathbf{q} = \mathbf{r} + \rho\mathbf{n},$$

so that the centre of the sphere in this case lies in the osculating plane at $\mathbf{r}$. In fact, it lies on the principal normal at $\mathbf{r}$. The osculating plane cuts the sphere in a great circle of radius ρ called the **circle of curvature**. The centre of this circle is called the **centre of curvature** and ρ is called the **radius of curvature**.

Again, by making a suitable choice of a, we can arrange that the sphere will intersect the curve in four coincident points. The additional condition will be $f'''(l) = 0$, or

$$\mathbf{n}' \cdot (\mathbf{r} - \mathbf{q}) + \mathbf{n} \cdot \mathbf{t} + \rho' = 0,$$

or $\qquad \{-(1/\rho)\mathbf{t} + (1/\tau)\mathbf{b}\} \cdot \{-\rho\mathbf{n} \mp (a^2 - \rho^2)^{\frac{1}{2}}\mathbf{b}\} + \rho' = 0,$

or $\qquad\qquad\qquad \mp (a^2 - \rho^2)^{\frac{1}{2}}/\tau + \rho' = 0,$

i.e., $\qquad\qquad\qquad a^2 = \rho^2 + \tau^2\rho'^2.$

In this case

$$\mathbf{q} = \mathbf{r} + \rho\mathbf{n} + \tau\rho'\mathbf{b}.$$

This point is the **centre of spherical curvature** and the radius $(\rho^2 + \tau^2\rho'^2)^{\frac{1}{2}}$ of this sphere is the **radius of spherical curvature**.

§ **18.** We shall now prove the theorem that *all curves whose curvature and torsion are the same functions of the arc are congruent.* In other words, apart from location in space, a curve is completely determined when its curvature and torsion are given as functions of the arc l measured from a fixed point on the curve.

Let the two curves be denoted by $\mathbf{r}(l)$ and $\mathbf{r}^*(l)$. We translate one of them so that the zero points $l = 0$ on the two curves coincide. We now rotate one of them about the zero point so that the moving trihedrals of the two curves coincide at the point $l = 0$. Now by Frenet's formulae

$$
\frac{d}{dl}(\mathbf{t} \cdot \mathbf{t}^* + \mathbf{n} \cdot \mathbf{n}^* + \mathbf{b} \cdot \mathbf{b}^*)
$$
$$
= \mathbf{t} \cdot \frac{\mathbf{n}^*}{\rho^*} + \frac{\mathbf{n}}{\rho} \cdot \mathbf{t}^* + \mathbf{n} \cdot \left(-\frac{\mathbf{t}^*}{\rho^*} + \frac{\mathbf{b}^*}{\tau^*} \right) + \left(-\frac{\mathbf{t}}{\rho} + \frac{\mathbf{b}}{\tau} \right) \cdot \mathbf{n}^*
$$
$$
- \mathbf{b} \cdot \frac{\mathbf{n}^*}{\tau^*} - \frac{\mathbf{n}}{\tau} \cdot \mathbf{b}^*.
$$

Further, the right-hand side is zero since by hypothesis $\rho^* = \rho$ and $\tau^* = \tau$. Hence

$$
\mathbf{t} \cdot \mathbf{t}^* + \mathbf{n} \cdot \mathbf{n}^* + \mathbf{b} \cdot \mathbf{b}^* = \text{constant},
$$

and the value of this constant is 3 since $\mathbf{t} = \mathbf{t}^*$, $\mathbf{n} = \mathbf{n}^*$, $\mathbf{b} = \mathbf{b}^*$ when $l = 0$. It follows that for any value of l we have

$$
\mathbf{t} = \mathbf{t}^*, \quad \mathbf{n} = \mathbf{n}^*, \quad \mathbf{b} = \mathbf{b}^*.
$$

From $\mathbf{t} = \mathbf{t}^*$, we have $\mathbf{r}' = \mathbf{r}^{*\prime}$ and therefore $\mathbf{r} = \mathbf{r}^* + \mathbf{a}$ where $\mathbf{a}$ is a constant vector which is evidently zero since $\mathbf{r} = \mathbf{r}^*$ at $l = 0$. Hence $\mathbf{r} = \mathbf{r}^*$ for all values of l. This proves the theorem.

The equations

$$
\rho = \rho(l), \quad \tau = \tau(l), \qquad . \qquad . \qquad . \qquad (12)
$$

which specify the curve, are called the **intrinsic equations** or **natural equations** of the curve. It can be shown further that, provided we restrict ρ to have positive values, a curve exists whose intrinsic equations are $\rho = \rho(l)$, $\tau = \tau(l)$, where ρ and τ are given continuous functions of l.

§ 19. The position vector of any point $\mathbf{r}(l)$ on a curve may be expanded in powers of l by using the vector form of Taylor's theorem. Thus

$$\mathbf{r}(l) = \mathbf{r}(0) + \frac{l}{1!}\mathbf{r}'(0) + \frac{l^2}{2!}\mathbf{r}''(0) + \frac{l^3}{3!}\mathbf{r}'''(0) + \ldots$$

$$= \mathbf{r}(0) + \frac{l}{1!}\mathbf{t}(0) + \frac{l^2}{2!}\frac{\mathbf{n}(0)}{\rho_0} + \frac{l^3}{3!}\left(-\frac{\mathbf{t}(0)}{\rho_0{}^2} - \frac{\rho'_0\mathbf{n}(0)}{\rho_0{}^2} + \frac{\mathbf{b}(0)}{\rho_0\tau_0} \right) + \ldots$$

for $\mathbf{r}'' = \dfrac{1}{\rho}\mathbf{n}$ and so $\mathbf{r}''' = \dfrac{1}{\rho}\left(-\dfrac{1}{\rho}\mathbf{t} + \dfrac{1}{\tau}\mathbf{b} \right) - \dfrac{\rho'}{\rho^2}\mathbf{n}$. If now we

choose the point $l = 0$ to be the origin and the directions of $\mathbf{t}, \mathbf{n}, \mathbf{b}$ at the origin to be the axes OX, OY, OZ, then the parametric equations of the curve take the form

$$\left. \begin{aligned} x &= l &&- \frac{1}{6\rho_0{}^2}l^3 + \ldots, \\ y &= \frac{1}{2\rho_0}l^2 &&- \frac{\rho'_0}{6\rho_0{}^2}l^3 + \ldots, \\ z &= &&\frac{1}{6\rho_0\tau_0}l^3 + \ldots. \end{aligned} \right\} \qquad \bullet \quad \bullet \quad (13)$$

These are called the **canonical equations** of the curve.

§ 20. It will be useful at this point to illustrate the preceding theory by applying it to the helix

$$x = a \cos \theta, \quad y = a \sin \theta, \quad z = a\,\theta \tan \alpha,$$

where θ is the variable parameter. Now $\theta = (z/a)\,\cot \alpha$, so the helix is part of the intersection of the two cylinders

$$x^2 + y^2 = a^2, \quad x = a \cos [(z/a)\,\cot \alpha].$$

Also

$$dl^2 = dx^2 + dy^2 + dz^2 = a^2(\sin^2 \theta + \cos^2 \theta + \tan^2 \alpha)d\theta^2 = a^2 \sec^2 \alpha\, d\theta^2,$$

so if we measure l from the point where $\theta = 0$, we have

$$l = \int_0^\theta a \sec a d\theta = a\theta \sec a \; ;$$

whence

$$\theta = (l/a) \cos a.$$

The helix is therefore represented by

$$\mathbf{r} = \qquad a \cos \left(\frac{l}{a} \cos a\right)\mathbf{i} \; + \qquad a \sin \left(\frac{l}{a} \cos a\right)\mathbf{j} + l \sin a \, \mathbf{k},$$

and

$$\mathbf{r}' = -\sin \left(\frac{l}{a} \cos a\right) \cos a \, \mathbf{i} \; + \cos \left(\frac{l}{a} \cos a\right) \cos a \, \mathbf{j} + \sin a \, \mathbf{k},$$

$$\mathbf{r}'' = -\cos \left(\frac{l}{a} \cos a\right) \frac{\cos^2 a}{a}\mathbf{i} \; - \sin \left(\frac{l}{a} \cos a\right) \frac{\cos^2 a}{a}\mathbf{j},$$

$$\mathbf{r}''' = \quad \sin \left(\frac{l}{a} \cos a\right) \frac{\cos^3 a}{a^2}\mathbf{i} \; - \cos \left(\frac{l}{a} \cos a\right) \frac{\cos^3 a}{a^2}\mathbf{j}.$$

The equation to the tangent at l is

$$\frac{x - a \cos [(l/a) \cos a]}{-\sin [(l/a) \cos a] \cos a} = \frac{y - a \sin [(l/a) \cos a]}{\cos [(l/a) \cos a] \cos a} = \frac{z - l \sin a}{\sin a}$$

or

$$\frac{x - a \cos \theta}{-\sin \theta} = \frac{y - a \sin \theta}{\cos \theta} = \frac{z - a\theta \tan a}{\tan a}.$$

The osculating plane is

$$\begin{vmatrix} x - a \cos \theta, & y - a \sin \theta, & z - a\theta \tan a \\ -\sin \theta, & \cos \theta, & \tan a \\ \cos \theta, & \sin \theta, & 0 \end{vmatrix} = 0.$$

Further $1/\rho^2 = \mathbf{r}'' \cdot \mathbf{r}'' = (\cos^4 a)/a^2$, so

$$\rho = a \sec^2 a,$$

showing that the curvature of the helix is constant.

Again $\qquad\qquad$ $[\mathbf{r}', \mathbf{r}'', \mathbf{r}''']$

$$= \begin{vmatrix} -\sin\theta\cos a, & \cos\theta\cos a, & \sin a \\ -(\cos\theta\cos^2 a)/a, & -(\sin\theta\cos^2 a)/a, & 0 \\ (\sin\theta\cos^3 a)/a^2, & -(\cos\theta\cos^3 a)/a^2, & 0 \end{vmatrix}$$

$$= (\sin a\cos^5 a)/a^3,$$

so $\qquad$ $1/\tau = \rho^2[\mathbf{r}', \mathbf{r}'', \mathbf{r}'''] = (\sin a\cos a)/a,$

showing that the torsion of a helix is also constant. Since $\rho' = 0$, the radius of spherical curvature is ρ.

§21. $\qquad\qquad$ Examples

(1) $y = f(x)$ is a plane curve. Show that the expressions

$$l = \int_{x_0}^{x} \sqrt{\left\{1 + \left(\frac{dy}{dx}\right)^2\right\}}\,dx \quad \text{and} \quad l = \int_{u_0}^{u} \sqrt{\left\{\frac{d\mathbf{r}}{du}\cdot\frac{d\mathbf{r}}{du}\right\}}\,du$$

are identical. Show also that the expressions

$$1/\rho^2 = \left(\frac{d^2y}{dx^2}\right)^2 \Big/ \left\{1 + \left(\frac{dy}{dx}\right)^2\right\}^3 \quad \text{and} \quad 1/\rho^2 = \mathbf{r}''\cdot\mathbf{r}''$$

are identical.

(2) Show that the radius of curvature of the twisted curve

$$x = \log\cos\theta, \quad y = \log\sin\theta, \quad z = \theta\sqrt{2}$$

at a point θ is $\sqrt{2}/\sin 2\theta$.

(3) Prove that the radius of curvature of the twisted curve

$$x = at(3 - t^2), \quad y = 3at^2, \quad z = at(3 + t^2), \quad a = \text{constant}$$

at a point t is $3a(1 + t^2)^2$.

(4) The twisted curve

$$x = a\cos\phi, \quad y = a\sin\phi, \quad z = c\cosh(a\phi/c)$$

lies on the cylinder $x^2 + y^2 = a^2$. Prove that the osculating plane at any point of the curve makes a constant angle with the tangent plane to the cylinder at that point.

(5) Show that $\tau = \infty$ is the condition that a curve be a plane curve.

(6) Show that the necessary and sufficient condition that a curve should lie on a sphere is

$$\frac{\rho}{\tau} + \frac{d}{dl}(\rho'\tau) = 0.$$

(7) If S is the locus of the centres of spherical curvature of a curve C, show that any tangent to S is perpendicular to the corresponding tangent to C.

SURFACES

§ 22. If we eliminate the independent parameters u and v from the three scalar equations

$$x = x(u, v), \quad y = y(u, v), \quad z = z(u, v), \qquad \bullet \quad (14)$$

which are the components of the vector equation

$$\mathbf{r} = \mathbf{r}(u, v), \quad . \qquad . \qquad . \qquad \bullet \quad (15)$$

we obtain in general a single equation of the form

$$\phi(x, y, z) = 0,$$

which represents a surface. That is to say, the equation (15) represents a surface, for the point (x, y, z) will lie on $\phi(x, y, z) = 0$ for any values of u and v. In particular all points on the surface for which u has the constant value u_1 form a curve which lies on the surface, for the equation

$$\mathbf{r} = \mathbf{r}(u_1, v)$$

is of the same type as equation (1), since it involves only one parameter v. We have thus an infinity of curves for which u is a constant and similarly an infinity of curves for which v is a constant. These are the **parametric lines** of the surface. u and v are the **curvilinear coordinates** of a point on the surface.

The vector $\dfrac{\partial \mathbf{r}}{\partial u}$ will be a tangent to the parametric line $v = \text{constant}$. We shall call this vector $\mathbf{r}_u$ and we denote the tangent vector $\dfrac{\partial \mathbf{r}}{\partial v}$ to a parametric line $u = \text{constant}$ by

$\mathbf{r}_v$. The vectors $\mathbf{r}_u$ and $\mathbf{r}_v$ are not in general unit vectors. We suppose that $\mathbf{r}_u$ and $\mathbf{r}_v$ do not coincide in direction, so that $\mathbf{r}_u \times \mathbf{r}_v \neq \mathbf{0}$. Now the equations

$$u = u(t), \quad v = v(t)$$

determine a curve on the surface, for x, y, z are then functions of a single parameter t. This curve is

$$\mathbf{r} = \mathbf{r}(u(t), v(t)),$$

and its tangent vector is

$$\frac{d\mathbf{r}}{dt} = \frac{du}{dt}\frac{\partial \mathbf{r}}{\partial u} + \frac{dv}{dt}\frac{\partial \mathbf{r}}{\partial v} = \frac{du}{dt}\mathbf{r}_u + \frac{dv}{dt}\mathbf{r}_v.$$

Also, since

$$\mathbf{r}_u \cdot \mathbf{r}_u \times \mathbf{r}_v = \mathbf{r}_v \cdot \mathbf{r}_u \times \mathbf{r}_v = 0,$$

this tangent vector is perpendicular to $\mathbf{r}_u \times \mathbf{r}_v$. Hence the tangent vector to any curve on the surface passing through $\mathbf{r}$ is perpendicular to $\mathbf{r}_u \times \mathbf{r}_v$, so that $\mathbf{r}_u \times \mathbf{r}_v$ is a vector which is normal to the tangent plane at $\mathbf{r}$. The **tangent plane** at a point $\mathbf{r}_1$ on the surface will have the equation

$$\mathbf{r} = \mathbf{r}_1 + h(\mathbf{r}_u)_1 + k(\mathbf{r}_v)_1 \quad . \quad . \quad . \quad (16)$$

where h and k are variable scalars. The equation to this tangent plane may also be written

$$[\mathbf{r} - \mathbf{r}_1, \ (\mathbf{r}_u)_1, \ (\mathbf{r}_v)_1] = 0.$$

Now by § 6, (14)

$$(\mathbf{r}_u \times \mathbf{r}_v)^2 = \mathbf{r}_u^2 \mathbf{r}_v^2 - (\mathbf{r}_u \cdot \mathbf{r}_v)^2 = EG - F^2,$$

where

$$E = \mathbf{r}_u \cdot \mathbf{r}_u, \quad F = \mathbf{r}_u \cdot \mathbf{r}_v, \quad G = \mathbf{r}_v \cdot \mathbf{r}_v, \quad . \quad (17)$$

so the length of $\mathbf{r}_u \times \mathbf{r}_v$ is $(EG - F^2)^{\frac{1}{2}}$. If $\mathbf{e}$ be the unit normal to the surface, then

$$\mathbf{e} = (\mathbf{r}_u \times \mathbf{r}_v)/(EG - F^2)^{\frac{1}{2}}. \quad . \quad . \quad (18)$$

If dl be the element of length between two points whose position vectors are $\mathbf{r}$ and $\mathbf{r} + d\mathbf{r}$, then

$$dl^2 = (d\mathbf{r})^2 = (\mathbf{r}_u du + \mathbf{r}_v dv)^2,$$

or $\quad\quad dl^2 = E du^2 + 2F du dv + G dv^2. \quad . \quad . \quad (19)$

(19) is called the **first fundamental quadratic form.**
When the surface is a plane and u and v are the rectangular
coordinates x and y, (19) reduces to $dl^2 = dx^2 + dy^2$, which is
simply the theorem of Pythagoras.

Again, if (u, v_1) and $(u + du, v_1)$ be two points on the same
parametric line $v = v_1$ then $dl^2 = E du^2$ since dv is zero ; so
the element of length in the direction of a parametric line
$v = $ constant is $dl = E^{\frac{1}{2}} du$. Similarly the element of length
between the two points (u_1, v) and $(u_1, v + dv)$ is given by
$dl = G^{\frac{1}{2}} dv$.

The length of $\mathbf{r}_u$ is $E^{\frac{1}{2}}$ so the unit tangent vector in the
direction $\mathbf{r}_u$ is $E^{-\frac{1}{2}}\mathbf{r}_u$, and the unit tangent vector in the direction $\mathbf{r}_v$ is $G^{-\frac{1}{2}}\mathbf{r}_v$. If the angle between the two parametric
lines through any point be ω then

$$\cos \omega = (EG)^{-\frac{1}{2}}\mathbf{r}_u \cdot \mathbf{r}_v = (F^2/EG)^{\frac{1}{2}}$$

and $$\sin \omega = (EG - F^2)^{\frac{1}{2}}/(EG)^{\frac{1}{2}}.$$

Consider a small quadrilateral whose vertices are the points

$$(u, v), \quad (u + du, v), \quad (u, v + dv), \quad (u + du, v + dv).$$

To a first approximation the opposite sides are equal
and we may regard the figure as a parallelogram whose
sides are of lengths $E^{\frac{1}{2}} du$ and $G^{\frac{1}{2}} dv$. The area ds * of the
small quadrilateral is therefore

$$ds = E^{\frac{1}{2}} du G^{\frac{1}{2}} dv (EG - F^2)^{\frac{1}{2}}/(EG)^{\frac{1}{2}} = (EG - F^2)^{\frac{1}{2}} du dv. \quad (20)$$

§ **23.** The vector $\mathbf{e}$ is not a constant vector although it
is of constant length.

$$-d\mathbf{r} \cdot d\mathbf{e} = -(\mathbf{r}_u du + \mathbf{r}_v dv) \cdot (\mathbf{e}_u du + \mathbf{e}_v dv)$$
$$= L du^2 + 2M du dv + N dv^2, \quad . \quad . \quad (21)$$

where

$$L = -\mathbf{r}_u \cdot \mathbf{e}_u, \quad 2M = -\mathbf{r}_u \cdot \mathbf{e}_v - \mathbf{r}_v \cdot \mathbf{e}_u, \quad N = -\mathbf{r}_v \cdot \mathbf{e}_v.$$

(21) is called the **second fundamental quadratic form.**

* Some authors use ds and dS to denote elements of length and
surface respectively.

Since $\mathbf{e} \cdot \mathbf{r}_u = 0$ and $\mathbf{e} \cdot \mathbf{r}_v = 0$, we have

$$\mathbf{e}_u \cdot \mathbf{r}_u + \mathbf{e} \cdot \mathbf{r}_{uu} = 0, \quad \mathbf{e}_u \cdot \mathbf{r}_v + \mathbf{e} \cdot \mathbf{r}_{vu} = 0,$$
$$\mathbf{e}_v \cdot \mathbf{r}_u + \mathbf{e} \cdot \mathbf{r}_{uv} = 0, \quad \mathbf{e}_v \cdot \mathbf{r}_v + \mathbf{e} \cdot \mathbf{r}_{vv} = 0.$$

Hence

$$\left.\begin{array}{l} L = \mathbf{e} \cdot \mathbf{r}_{uu} = [\mathbf{r}_u,\ \mathbf{r}_v,\ \mathbf{r}_{uu}]/(EG - F^2)^{\frac{1}{2}}, \\ M = \mathbf{e} \cdot \mathbf{r}_{uv} = [\mathbf{r}_u,\ \mathbf{r}_v,\ \mathbf{r}_{uv}]/(EG - F^2)^{\frac{1}{2}}, \\ N = \mathbf{e} \cdot \mathbf{r}_{vv} = [\mathbf{r}_u,\ \mathbf{r}_v,\ \mathbf{r}_{vv}]/(EG - F^2)^{\frac{1}{2}}. \end{array}\right\} \qquad . \quad (22)$$

§ 24. For any curve on the surface

$$\mathbf{t} \cdot \mathbf{e} = 0.$$

Differentiating this relation with respect to l and applying Frenet's formulae, we have

$$\frac{1}{\rho}\mathbf{n} \cdot \mathbf{e} = -\frac{d\mathbf{r}}{dl} \cdot \frac{d\mathbf{e}}{dl} = -\frac{d\mathbf{r} \cdot d\mathbf{e}}{dl^2};$$

or

$$\frac{1}{\rho}\mathbf{n} \cdot \mathbf{e} = \frac{L\,du^2 + 2M\,du\,dv + N\,dv^2}{E\,du^2 + 2F\,du\,dv + G\,dv^2}.$$

The right-hand side of this equation is a scalar function depending only upon the position (u, v) on the surface and upon the direction (given by du/dv) of the curve through this point. In other words,

$$\frac{1}{\rho}\mathbf{n} \cdot \mathbf{e}$$

has the same value at any point P for all curves on the surface passing through P in a given direction. Further, $\mathbf{n} \cdot \mathbf{e}$ is the cosine of the angle θ between the osculating plane and the normal to the surface. Consider all plane sections of the surface through a given tangent line. If θ is the angle between the osculating plane of the curve of intersection and the normal to the surface, then

$$\cos \theta / \rho = \text{constant}.$$

In particular, if R be the radius of curvature of the normal section, which is the section for which $\cos\theta = 1$, then

$$\rho = R\cos\theta. \qquad . \qquad . \qquad . \qquad (23)$$

From this we have **Meusnier's theorem** that *the circles of curvature of all plane sections through the same line element of a surface lie on a sphere.*

From the foregoing equations we have

$$\frac{1}{R} = \frac{Ldu^2 + 2Mdudv + Ndv^2}{Edu^2 + 2Fdudv + Gdv^2},$$

whence

$$(RL - E)du^2 + 2(RM - F)dudv + (RN - G)dv^2 = 0, \quad (24)$$

giving two directions du/dv for a given value of R. These will coincide if (24) has a double root, in which case

$$\left.\begin{array}{l}(RL - E)du + (RM - F)dv = 0 \\ (RM - F)du + (RN - G)dv = 0\end{array}\right\}, \quad . \quad . \quad (25)$$

which can only be true if

$$(RL - E)(RN - G) = (RM - F)^2,$$

i.e., if

$$R^2(LN - M^2) + R(2MF - LG - NE) + (EG - F^2) = 0.$$

This equation gives at any point on the surface two values R_1 and R_2 which we call the **principal radii of curvature** at that point. Eliminating R from (25), we find that the **principal directions** at any point are obtained from

$$(LF - ME)du^2 + (LG - NE)dudv + (MG - NF)dv^2 = 0. \quad (26)$$

A **line of curvature** is a line whose tangent at any point has a direction coinciding with a principal direction at that point. (26) is therefore the differential equation of all lines of curvature.

We write

$$K = 1/R_1 R_2 = (LN - M^2)/(EG - F^2),$$

and $\quad 2H = 1/R_1 + 1/R_2 = (EN - 2FM + GL)/(EG - F^2).$

K is called the **Gaussian curvature** and H is called the **average curvature.**

§ 25. The vectors $\mathbf{r}_u$ and $\mathbf{r}_v$ depend only upon the position (u, v) on the surface at which they are calculated ; $\dfrac{du}{dl}$ and $\dfrac{dv}{dl}$ on the other hand depend upon the direction of dl. If $\dfrac{du}{dl}, \dfrac{dv}{dl}$ refer to a curve C_1 and $\dfrac{\delta u}{\delta l}, \dfrac{\delta v}{\delta l}$ refer to a second curve C_2, then the unit tangents to these two curves at their point of intersection are

$$\mathbf{r}_u\frac{du}{dl} + \mathbf{r}_v\frac{dv}{dl} \quad \text{and} \quad \mathbf{r}_u\frac{\delta u}{\delta l} + \mathbf{r}_v\frac{\delta v}{\delta l}.$$

The condition that C_1 and C_2 cut orthogonally is that the scalar product of their tangent vectors be zero, i.e.,

$$(\mathbf{r}_u \cdot \mathbf{r}_u)\frac{du}{dl}\frac{\delta u}{\delta l} + (\mathbf{r}_u \cdot \mathbf{r}_v)\left(\frac{du}{dl}\frac{\delta v}{\delta l} + \frac{\delta u}{\delta l}\frac{dv}{dl}\right) + (\mathbf{r}_v \cdot \mathbf{r}_v)\frac{dv}{dl}\frac{\delta v}{\delta l} = 0,$$

or

$$E\frac{du}{dv}\frac{\delta u}{\delta v} + F\left(\frac{du}{dv} + \frac{\delta u}{\delta v}\right) + G = 0. \qquad \cdot \quad \cdot \quad (27)$$

Now if $\dfrac{du}{dv}$ and $\dfrac{\delta u}{\delta v}$ be the two roots of (26), then

$$\frac{du}{dv}\frac{\delta u}{\delta v} = \frac{MG - NF}{LF - ME} \quad \text{and} \quad \frac{du}{dv} + \frac{\delta u}{\delta v} = -\frac{LG - NE}{LF - ME}.$$

These values satisfy (27) since

$$E(MG - NF) - F(LG - NE) + G(LF - ME) \equiv 0.$$

Hence the principal directions at any point are perpendicular and therefore the lines of curvature form an orthogonal net.

If we choose the lines of curvature as the parametric lines, then $F = \mathbf{r}_u \cdot \mathbf{r}_v = 0$ and the differential equations of the lines of curvature are $du = 0$ and $dv = 0$ so that (26) takes the form $du\, dv = 0$. It follows that $LF - ME = MG - NF = 0$. Since E, F, G are not all zero, we must have $M = 0$. Hence *the necessary and sufficient conditions that the lines of curvature be the parametric lines are*

$$F = M = 0.$$

§ 26. As we have said, the unit tangent vector to a curve $\mathbf{r}(l)$ is

$$\mathbf{r}_u \frac{du}{dl} + \mathbf{r}_v \frac{dv}{dl},$$

and the unit tangent to the curve $v = $ constant is

$$E^{-\frac{1}{2}}\mathbf{r}_u.$$

If θ_v is the angle between these two curves,

$$\cos \theta_v = \left(\mathbf{r}_u \cdot \mathbf{r}_u \frac{du}{dl} + \mathbf{r}_u \cdot \mathbf{r}_v \frac{dv}{dl}\right)\bigg/ E^{\frac{1}{2}} = \left(E\frac{du}{dl} + F\frac{dv}{dl}\right)\bigg/ E^{\frac{1}{2}}.$$

Similarly

$$\cos \theta_u = \left(F\frac{du}{dl} + G\frac{dv}{dl}\right)\bigg/ G^{\frac{1}{2}}.$$

If R_u and R_v denote the radii of curvature of the normal sections through the curves $u = $ constant and $v = $ constant, then since $du = 0$ for the curve $u = $ constant and $dv = 0$ for the curve $v = $ constant, we have from (24)

$$\frac{1}{R_u} = \frac{N}{G}, \quad \frac{1}{R_v} = \frac{L}{E}.$$

When the parametric lines are the lines of curvature, then $F = 0$, so

$$\cos \theta_v = E^{\frac{1}{2}}\frac{du}{dl}, \quad \cos \theta_u = G^{\frac{1}{2}}\frac{dv}{dl} ;$$

also $\cos \theta_v = \sin \theta_u$ since the lines of curvature form an orthogonal net. In this case R_u and R_v are the principal radii of curvature R_1 and R_2, so

$$\frac{\cos^2 \theta}{R_1} + \frac{\sin^2 \theta}{R_2} = \frac{Ldu^2 + Ndv^2}{dl^2},$$

where θ is written for θ_u. But since in the present case $M = 0$, we have from (24)

$$\frac{1}{R} = \frac{L du^2 + N dv^2}{dl^2}.$$

Combining the last two equations we obtain **Euler's theorem,** viz.

$$\frac{1}{R} = \frac{\cos^2 \theta}{R_1} + \frac{\sin^2 \theta}{R_2},$$

which gives the curvature of any normal section in terms of the principal curvatures at that point and the angle between the curve and the principal direction whose radius of curvature is R_1.

§ 27. It is evident from the equation

$$\frac{1}{R} = \frac{L du^2 + 2M du dv + N dv^2}{dl^2}$$

that R has the same sign as $L du^2 + 2M du dv + N dv^2$. If at any point $LN > M^2$, then R has the same sign for all directions and the centres of curvature of all normal sections at (u, v) lie on the same side of the surface. Such points on the surface are called **elliptical points.** If on the other hand $LN < M^2$, some of the centres of curvature will lie on one side of the surface and some on the other. Such points are called **hyperbolic points.** Points for which $LN = M^2$ are **parabolic points.**

At any point, the directions for which $L du^2 + 2M du dv + N dv^2 = 0$ will separate the curves with positive curvature from those with negative curvature. These are the **asymptotic directions** at the point. A line whose direction is an asymptotic direction at each point of it is called an **asymptotic line.** The differential equation of all asymptotic lines is therefore

$$L du^2 + 2M du dv + N dv^2 = 0. \qquad . \qquad . \quad (28)$$

D

In general there are two asymptotic lines through each point of the surface and we shall show that the angles between them are bisected by the lines of curvature. To show this we take the lines of curvature to be the parametric lines. The value of du/dv for any curve will now be $(G/E)^{\frac{1}{2}} \tan \theta$, where θ is the angle between the curve and the line of curvature $u = $ constant. The asymptotic lines now have the differential equation $L du^2 + N dv^2 = 0$ so that $du/dv = \pm (-N/L)^{\frac{1}{2}}$, showing that the two asymptotic directions make equal angles with the line of curvature $u = $ constant. In the same way they make equal angles with the curvature line $v = $ constant.

From the equation (28) we find that for an asymptotic line

$$\frac{1}{\rho}\mathbf{n} \cdot \mathbf{e} = 0.$$

If $\rho \neq \infty$, then $\mathbf{e}$ is perpendicular to $\mathbf{n}$ as well as to $\mathbf{t}$ so that the tangent plane is the osculating plane. If $\rho = \infty$, the line is straight at this point and any plane through the line may be taken as the osculating plane. We may in fact take the tangent plane as the osculating plane. Hence *the asymptotic lines of a surface are the curves on the surface whose osculating planes coincide with the tangent planes at each point of the curve.*

§ **28.** We shall illustrate the theory of surfaces by considering the paraboloid of revolution $z = x^2 + y^2$. We may take the parametric equations to be

$$x = u \cos v, \quad y = u \sin v, \quad z = u^2.$$

Then

$$\mathbf{r} = u \cos v \, \mathbf{i} + u \sin v \, \mathbf{j} + u^2 \mathbf{k},$$

$$\mathbf{r}_u = \cos v \, \mathbf{i} + \sin v \, \mathbf{j} + 2u \mathbf{k},$$

$$\mathbf{r}_v = -u \sin v \, \mathbf{i} + u \cos v \, \mathbf{j},$$

whence

$$E = 1 + 4u^2, \quad F = 0, \quad G = u^2$$

and

$$(EG - F^2)^{\frac{1}{2}} = u(1 + 4u^2)^{\frac{1}{2}}.$$

Further $\qquad$ $\mathbf{r}_{uu} = \qquad\qquad 2\mathbf{k}$,

$\qquad\qquad \mathbf{r}_{uv} = - \quad \sin v \quad \mathbf{i} + \quad \cos v \, \mathbf{j}$,

$\qquad\qquad \mathbf{r}_{vv} = - u \cos v \quad \mathbf{i} - u \sin v \, \mathbf{j}$.

So

$\qquad [\mathbf{r}_u, \, \mathbf{r}_v, \, \mathbf{r}_{uu}] = 2u, \qquad L = 2/(1 + 4u^2)^{\frac{1}{2}},$

$\qquad [\mathbf{r}_u, \, \mathbf{r}_v, \, \mathbf{r}_{uv}] = 0, \qquad M = 0,$

$\qquad [\mathbf{r}_u, \, \mathbf{r}_v, \, \mathbf{r}_{vv}] = 2u^3, \qquad N = 2u^2/(1 + 4u^2)^{\frac{1}{2}}.$

Since $F = M = 0$, the lines of curvature are $u = $ constant and $v = $ constant.

The asymptotic lines are given by $du^2 + u^2 dv^2 = 0$. These are imaginary since $LN > M^2$. All points on the surface are elliptical.

§ 29. Examples

(1) Find the lines of curvature on the surface

$$x = a(u + v), \quad y = b(u - v), \quad z = uv.$$

$[\log (u + \sqrt{a^2 + b^2 + u^2}) = \pm \log (v + \sqrt{a^2 + b^2 + v^2}) + \log c].$

Show that the parametric lines are the asymptotic lines, and that these are straight lines.

(2) Show that the asymptotic lines of the hyperboloid

$$x = a \cos \theta \sec \psi, \quad y = b \sin \theta \sec \psi, \quad z = c \tan \psi$$

are given by $\theta \pm \psi = $ constant.

(3) Show that the differential equation of the lines of curvature of the cylindroid $z(x^2 + y^2) = axy$ is $dr^2 + 2r \tan 2\theta \, dr d\theta - (r^2 + a^2 \cos^2 2\theta) d\theta^2 = 0$, where $r^2 = (x^2 + y^2)$ and $\theta = \tan^{-1} (y/x)$.

(4) The parametric equations of the helicoid are

$$x = u \cos v, \quad y = u \sin v, \quad z = cv.$$

Show that the asymptotic lines are $u = $ constant, $v = $ constant, and that the lines of curvature are $u + \sqrt{u^2 + c^2} = A e^{\pm v}$, A being a constant. Show that the principal radii are $\pm (u^2 + c^2)/c$.

(5) Show that the principal radii of curvature of the right conoid

$$x = u \cos v, \quad y = u \sin v, \quad z = f(v)$$

are given by the roots of the equation

$$f'^2 R^2 + u f''(u^2 + f'^2)^{\frac{1}{2}} R - (u^2 + f'^2)^2 = 0.$$

(6) Prove that the principal radii of curvature at every point of the surface $z = y \tan (x/a)$ are equal and opposite, and that they have a constant value at all points on the surface which also lie on the cylinder $y^2 + z^2 = c^2$.

(7) Use equation (20) to find the areas of a circle and of a sphere.

(8) Deduce the formula $\int 2\pi y (1 + y'^2)^{\frac{1}{2}} dx$ for the area of a surface of revolution.

(9) Show that the portion of the curve $u = v$ lying on the surface

$$x = u \cos v, \quad y = u \sin v, \quad z = u\sqrt{3}$$

which lies between $z = 0$ and $z = 2\sqrt{3}$ is of length $2 \sinh^{-1} 1$.

CHAPTER III

APPLICATIONS TO MECHANICS

§ 30. SUPPOSE that a particle is at the point P, whose position vector is $\mathbf{r}$, at time t and that at time $t + \delta t$ the particle is at P' whose position vector is $\mathbf{r} + \delta \mathbf{r}$. Then $\mathbf{r} + \delta \mathbf{r} = \mathbf{r} + \overline{PP'}$, so that $\overline{PP'} = \delta \mathbf{r}$. Now the velocity vector of the particle is

$$\lim_{\delta t \to 0} \frac{\overline{PP'}}{\delta t} = \lim_{\delta t \to 0} \frac{\delta \mathbf{r}}{\delta t} = \dot{\mathbf{r}},$$

where the dot stands for differentiation with respect to the time t. The components of the velocity vector $\dot{\mathbf{r}}$ in the coordinate directions are $\dot{x}, \dot{y}, \dot{z}$. In the same way $\ddot{\mathbf{r}}$ is the acceleration vector and its components in the coordinate directions are $\ddot{x}, \ddot{y}, \ddot{z}$. In § 39 we shall obtain the components of velocity and acceleration in other directions. It follows from the preceding that velocities and accelerations obey the vector law of addition.

Newton's second law of motion may be stated in the form $\mathbf{F} = \dot{\mathbf{p}}$, where $\mathbf{p}$ is the momentum $m\dot{\mathbf{r}}$ of the particle of mass m, whose position vector is $\mathbf{r}$ and which is acted upon by a resultant force $\mathbf{F}$. Since m is a scalar, it follows that $\mathbf{p}$ and therefore $\mathbf{F}$ are vectors. This indicates that forces which act on a particle are compounded by the parallelogram law. It usually happens that the mass of the particle remains constant during the motion, in which case Newton's law takes the familiar form

$$\mathbf{F} = m\ddot{\mathbf{r}}, \quad . \quad . \quad . \quad . \quad (1)$$

or $\qquad\qquad force = mass \times acceleration$

The single vector equation (1) is equivalent to three scalar equations

$$F_x = m\ddot{x}, \quad F_y = m\ddot{y}, \quad F_z = m\ddot{z},$$

and the integration of these equations where F_x, F_y, F_z are known functions of x, y, z, $\dot{x}$, $\dot{y}$, $\dot{z}$ and t, is one of the major problems of elementary mechanics.

§ **31.** Two forces which act at the same point P of a rigid body are equivalent to a single force at P which is the vector sum of the two forces, but two forces which act at different points of a rigid body are not necessarily equivalent to a single force. Forces are in fact **localised vectors**. That is to say, a force is associated with a definite point of application. Forces combine according to the vector addition law provided that they act at the same point.

If $\mathbf{w}$ be a localised vector, $\mathbf{r}$ its point of application and $\mathbf{a}$ any point in space, then we define the moment of $\mathbf{w}$ about $\mathbf{a}$ to be the vector

$$(\mathbf{r} - \mathbf{a}) \times \mathbf{w}.$$

The moment of $\mathbf{w}$ about the origin is evidently $\mathbf{r} \times \mathbf{w}$. From our definition of a vector product it follows that the magnitude of the moment of $\mathbf{w}$ about $\mathbf{a}$ is pw (fig. 7), where p is the perpendicular distance of $\mathbf{a}$ from the line of action of $\mathbf{w}$.

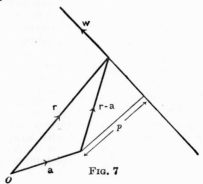

Fig. 7

We shall see in § 36 that the motion of a rigid body is completely determined when we know $\mathbf{F}$ the vector sum of all the forces acting on it and $\mathbf{G}_O$ the resultant moment about the origin of all the forces acting on it. Now $\mathbf{F}$ and $\mathbf{G}_O$ will be unaltered if we replace any force acting at some point of the body by an equal force acting at some other point of the body which is on the line of action of the force. It follows that the motion of a body will be unaffected by displacing any force along its own line of action. We may therefore conclude that two forces whose lines of action intersect in a point P are equivalent to a single force, the vector sum of the two forces, whose line of action also passes through P.

Apart from the exceptional case of a couple mentioned below, two parallel forces with different lines of action are

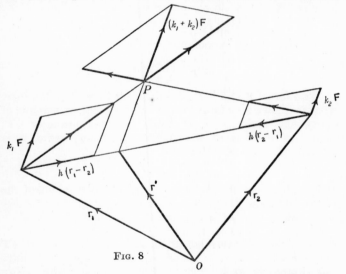

FIG. 8

equivalent to a single force as we shall now show (fig. 8). Let the forces be $k_1\mathbf{F}$ and $k_2\mathbf{F}$ and let $\mathbf{r}_1$, $\mathbf{r}_2$ be points on

their lines of action. We can introduce equal and opposite
forces $h(\mathbf{r}_1 - \mathbf{r}_2)$ at $\mathbf{r}_1$ and $h(\mathbf{r}_2 - \mathbf{r}_1)$ at $\mathbf{r}_2$ without altering
the circumstances in any significant way. The lines of
action of the resultant $k_1\mathbf{F} + h(\mathbf{r}_1 - \mathbf{r}_2)$ at $\mathbf{r}_1$ and the resultant
$k_2\mathbf{F} + h(\mathbf{r}_2 - \mathbf{r}_1)$ at $\mathbf{r}_2$ will intersect at a point P unless these
two resultants are parallel; that is to say, unless $k_1 = -k_2$,
which is the case of a couple. Excepting this case for
the present, the system is equivalent to a single force
$k_1\mathbf{F} + h(\mathbf{r}_1 - \mathbf{r}_2) + k_2\mathbf{F} + h(\mathbf{r}_2 - \mathbf{r}_1)$ or $(k_1 + k_2)\mathbf{F}$ at P. It is not
necessary to find P itself for it is sufficient to locate any
point on the line of action of the resultant $(k_1 + k_2)\mathbf{F}$. To
find the position vector $\mathbf{r}'$ of such a point, we observe that
the moment about O of the resultant must equal the resultant
of the moments about O of the original forces. This follows
from the fact that moments being defined as vectors must
be added according to the parallelogram law. Thus

$$\mathbf{r}' \times (k_1 + k_2)\mathbf{F} = \mathbf{r}_1 \times k_1\mathbf{F} + \mathbf{r}_2 \times k_2\mathbf{F}.$$

Evidently one solution of this equation is

$$\mathbf{r}' = \frac{k_1\mathbf{r}_1 + k_2\mathbf{r}_2}{k_1 + k_2}.$$

Two forces $\mathbf{F}$ and $-\mathbf{F}$ with different lines of action form
what is known as a **couple**. If $\mathbf{r}_1$ be a point on the line of
action of $\mathbf{F}$ and $\mathbf{r}_2$ be a point on the line of action of $-\mathbf{F}$,
then the moment of the couple about any point $\mathbf{a}$ is
$(\mathbf{r}_1 - \mathbf{a}) \times \mathbf{F} - (\mathbf{r}_2 - \mathbf{a}) \times \mathbf{F}$, or

$$(\mathbf{r}_1 - \mathbf{r}_2) \times \mathbf{F}.$$

It is to be observed that this vector is independent of the
choice of $\mathbf{a}$ and that its magnitude is pF where p is the
perpendicular distance between the two lines of action.

§ **32.** Consider a force $\mathbf{F}$ at $\mathbf{r}$. Introduce forces $+\mathbf{F}$
and $-\mathbf{F}$ at O. Since these are equal and opposite we have
not altered the existing state of affairs in any way. Now
$+\mathbf{F}$ at $\mathbf{r}$ and $-\mathbf{F}$ at O are equivalent to a couple $\mathbf{r} \times \mathbf{F}$,
hence a force $\mathbf{F}$ at $\mathbf{r}$ is equivalent to a force $\mathbf{F}$ at O together

with a couple $\mathbf{r} \times \mathbf{F}$. If now we have a system of forces $\mathbf{F}_1$ at $\mathbf{r}_1$, $\mathbf{F}_2$ at $\mathbf{r}_2, \ldots$, these are together equivalent to forces $\mathbf{F}_1$, $\mathbf{F}_2, \ldots$ all acting at O together with the couples $\mathbf{r}_1 \times \mathbf{F}_1$, $\mathbf{r}_2 \times \mathbf{F}_2, \ldots$ Hence the system of forces is equivalent to a single force $\Sigma \mathbf{F}_i$ at O together with a single couple $\Sigma \mathbf{r}_i \times \mathbf{F}_i$. Thus *any system of forces is reducible to a force which acts at an arbitrary point O together with a couple.*

Let us write $\mathbf{F} = \Sigma \mathbf{F}_i$ and $\mathbf{G} = \Sigma \mathbf{r}_i \times \mathbf{F}_i$. It may of course happen that one or both of $\mathbf{F}$ and $\mathbf{G}$ are zero. If $\mathbf{F} = \mathbf{G} = \mathbf{0}$, then the system of forces is in equilibrium. $\mathbf{F}$ and $\mathbf{G}$ will not in general have the same direction. The angle between them is given by

$$\cos \theta = (\mathbf{F}.\ \mathbf{G})/FG. \qquad \bullet \qquad \bullet \qquad \bullet \qquad (2)$$

As we choose our origin O in different places, $\mathbf{F}$ will not alter but the corresponding $\mathbf{G}$ will change. Suppose we choose a new origin O' whose position vector relative to O is $\mathbf{r}$; then the position vector of O relative to O' is $-\mathbf{r}$. Now $\mathbf{F}$ at O is equivalent to $\mathbf{F}$ at O' together with a couple $-\mathbf{r} \times \mathbf{F}$, so the system may be reduced to a force $\mathbf{F}$ at O' together with a couple $\mathbf{G} - (\mathbf{r} \times \mathbf{F})$.

We now wish to find whether there are any points O' for which the resultant couple has the same direction as the resultant force. In other words, are there vectors $\mathbf{r}$ for which

$$\mathbf{G} - (\mathbf{r} \times \mathbf{F}) = \lambda \mathbf{F},$$

where λ is a scalar multiplier ? If so, then

$$\mathbf{G}.\ \mathbf{F} - \mathbf{r} \times \mathbf{F}.\ \mathbf{F} = \lambda \mathbf{F}.\ \mathbf{F}$$

and $\lambda = (\mathbf{G}.\ \mathbf{F})/(\mathbf{F}.\ \mathbf{F})$ for $(\mathbf{r} \times \mathbf{F}.\ \mathbf{F}) = 0$; so

$$\mathbf{r} \times \mathbf{F} = \mathbf{G} - \{(\mathbf{G}.\ \mathbf{F})/(\mathbf{F}.\ \mathbf{F})\}\mathbf{F}.$$

Hence $\qquad\qquad (\mathbf{r} \times \mathbf{F}) \times \mathbf{F} = \mathbf{G} \times \mathbf{F}$

since $\mathbf{F} \times \mathbf{F} = \mathbf{0}$. Using § 5 (11), we have

$$(\mathbf{F}.\ \mathbf{F})\mathbf{r} - (\mathbf{F}.\ \mathbf{r})\mathbf{F} = \mathbf{F} \times \mathbf{G}.$$

There are many solutions for $\mathbf{r}$ but if in particular $\mathbf{F}.\ \mathbf{r} = 0$, then $\mathbf{r} = (\mathbf{F} \times \mathbf{G})/(\mathbf{F}.\ \mathbf{F})$ so that $\mathbf{r}$ is perpendicular to both

F and **G**. The most general solution is

$$\mathbf{r} = \frac{\mathbf{F} \times \mathbf{G}}{\mathbf{F} \cdot \mathbf{F}} + k\mathbf{F}, \quad \cdot \quad \cdot \quad \cdot \quad \cdot \quad (3)$$

k being an arbitrary scalar. We have therefore a line of points whose equation is (3), at any of which the resultant force and the resultant couple have the same direction. The direction of the line is that of **F** and one point on it is $\mathbf{r} = (\mathbf{F} \times \mathbf{G})/\mathbf{F}^2$. This line is called **Poinsot's central axis** for the given system of forces.

A force acting along a line together with a couple about a parallel line constitutes a **wrench**. We have shown that in general a system of forces is equivalent to a wrench. The **pitch** of the wrench is the ratio of the couple to the force, which in the case just considered is λ or $(\mathbf{G} \cdot \mathbf{F})/\mathbf{F}^2$.

In the two-dimensional case we invariably have $\mathbf{G} \cdot \mathbf{F} = 0$, so that a two-dimensional system of forces always reduces to a single force unless **F** vanishes, in which case the system reduces to a single couple **G**. It may happen of course that both **F** and **G** vanish.

§ 33. We now consider a system of n particles of which the ith has mass m_i and is situated at $\mathbf{r}_i$ at time t. Its velocity and acceleration are respectively $\dot{\mathbf{r}}_i$ and $\ddot{\mathbf{r}}_i$. We denote the total mass of the system Σm_i by M and define the position $\bar{\mathbf{r}}$ of the **mass centre** or centre of inertia by the equation

$$M\bar{\mathbf{r}} = \Sigma m_i \mathbf{r}_i. \quad \cdot \quad \cdot \quad \cdot \quad (4)$$

It follows that the velocity and acceleration of the mass centre are given by

$$M\dot{\bar{\mathbf{r}}} = \Sigma m_i \dot{\mathbf{r}}_i, \quad M\ddot{\bar{\mathbf{r}}} = \Sigma m_i \ddot{\mathbf{r}}_i.$$

That the position of the mass centre Q does not depend upon the origin chosen will be clear from the following argument. Let **a** be the position vector relative to O of a new origin O' and let us indicate all position vectors relative to O' with dashes. If the position vector of the mass centre Q' relative to O' be $\bar{\mathbf{r}}'$, then

$$M\bar{\mathbf{r}}' = \Sigma m_i \mathbf{r}'_i = \Sigma m_i(\mathbf{r}_i - \mathbf{a}) = \Sigma m_i \mathbf{r}_i - M\mathbf{a} = M(\bar{\mathbf{r}} - \mathbf{a}).$$

Hence $\bar{\mathbf{r}}' = \bar{\mathbf{r}} - \mathbf{a}$ showing that Q' coincides with Q.

We shall sometimes have occasion to choose the mass centre as origin. If $\boldsymbol{\rho}_i$ be the position vector of the mass m_i in such a case, then $\bar{\boldsymbol{\rho}} = \mathbf{0}$, from which it follows that

$$\Sigma m_i \boldsymbol{\rho}_i = \Sigma m_i \dot{\boldsymbol{\rho}}_i = \Sigma m_i \ddot{\boldsymbol{\rho}}_i = \mathbf{0}. \quad . \quad . \quad . \quad (5)$$

We may imagine that each particle of the system acts on each other particle of the system. According to **Newton's third law of motion** these forces are equal and opposite and have the same line of action. If $\mathbf{F}_{ij}$ denotes the force acting on the mass m_i due to the mass m_j then we may express Newton's law in the following equations :

$$\mathbf{F}_{ij} = \lambda_{ij}(\mathbf{r}_i - \mathbf{r}_j), \quad \lambda_{ij} = \lambda_{ji}$$

These may be expressed slightly differently in the form

$$\mathbf{F}_{ij} + \mathbf{F}_{ji} = \mathbf{0}, \quad . \quad . \quad . \quad . \quad (6)$$
$$(\mathbf{r}_i - \mathbf{r}_j) \times \mathbf{F}_{ij} = \mathbf{0}.$$

Combining these equations we have immediately

$$\mathbf{r}_i \times \mathbf{F}_{ij} + \mathbf{r}_j \times \mathbf{F}_{ji} = \mathbf{0}. \quad . \quad . \quad . \quad (7)$$

In addition to the forces just mentioned each particle may experience an external force. If we denote the external force on the mass m_i by $\mathbf{F}_{ii}$, then the equations of motion of the n particles become

$$\sum_j \mathbf{F}_{ij} = m_i \ddot{\mathbf{r}}_i, \quad i = 1, 2, \ldots, n. \quad . \quad . \quad . \quad (8)$$

Adding these n equations together we obtain

$$\sum_{i,j} \mathbf{F}_{ij} = \sum_i m_i \ddot{\mathbf{r}}_i = M\ddot{\bar{\mathbf{r}}}.$$

But by (6) all the forces in the double summation cancel in pairs with the exception of the external forces and $\sum_i \mathbf{F}_{ii}$ is the total external force $\mathbf{F}$ which acts on the system. Thus we have the important result

$$\mathbf{F} = M\ddot{\bar{\mathbf{r}}}, \quad . \quad . \quad . \quad . \quad (9)$$

which states that the *mass centre of a system of particles moves as if all the mass were concentrated at that point and as if all the external forces acted there.* We may also express (9) in the form

$$\mathbf{F} = \dot{\mathbf{p}} \qquad . \qquad . \qquad . \qquad . \qquad . \qquad (10)$$

where $\mathbf{p} \equiv M\dot{\bar{\mathbf{r}}} = \Sigma m_i \dot{\mathbf{r}}_i$ is the total momentum of the system.

§ 34. From (8) we find that

$$\sum_j \mathbf{r}_i \times \mathbf{F}_{ij} = m_i \mathbf{r}_i \times \ddot{\mathbf{r}}_i, \quad i = 1, 2, \ldots, n,$$

and adding these n equations we obtain

$$\sum_{i,j} \mathbf{r}_i \times \mathbf{F}_{ij} = \sum_i m_i \mathbf{r}_i \times \ddot{\mathbf{r}}_i.$$

By (7) all the terms on the left-hand side cancel with the exception of $\sum_i \mathbf{r}_i \times \mathbf{F}_{ii}$ which is simply the resultant moment $\mathbf{G}_O$ of the external forces about O. Since $\dot{\mathbf{r}}_i \times \dot{\mathbf{r}}_i = \mathbf{0}$, the right-hand side may be written $\dot{\mathbf{h}}_O$, where

$$\mathbf{h}_O = \Sigma \mathbf{r}_i \times (m_i \dot{\mathbf{r}}_i).$$

Evidently $\mathbf{h}_O$ is the resultant moment of the momentum of the system about O. It follows that

$$\mathbf{G}_O = \dot{\mathbf{h}}_O, \qquad . \qquad . \qquad . \qquad . \qquad (11)$$

which states that *the resultant moment of the external forces about any fixed point O is equal to the rate of change of the total moment of momentum about O.* We now show that this theorem is also true if both moments are taken about the mass centre Q which may of course be in motion. Choosing the mass centre as origin we write

$$\mathbf{r}_i = \bar{\mathbf{r}} + \boldsymbol{\rho}_i.$$

Now $\qquad \Sigma \mathbf{r}_i \times \mathbf{F}_{ii} = \Sigma(\bar{\mathbf{r}} + \boldsymbol{\rho}_i) \times \mathbf{F}_{ii} = \bar{\mathbf{r}} \times \mathbf{F} + \Sigma \boldsymbol{\rho}_i \times \mathbf{F}_{ii},$

whence $\qquad \mathbf{G}_O = \bar{\mathbf{r}} \times \mathbf{F} + \mathbf{G}_Q, \qquad . \qquad . \qquad . \qquad (12)$

where $\mathbf{G}_Q$ is the resultant moment of the external forces about the mass centre. Also

$$\Sigma \mathbf{r}_i \times m_i \dot{\mathbf{r}}_i = \Sigma(\bar{\mathbf{r}} + \boldsymbol{\rho}_i) \times m_i(\dot{\bar{\mathbf{r}}} + \dot{\boldsymbol{\rho}}_i)$$
$$= \bar{\mathbf{r}} \times M\dot{\bar{\mathbf{r}}} + \bar{\mathbf{r}} \times (\Sigma m_i \dot{\boldsymbol{\rho}}_i) + (\Sigma m_i \boldsymbol{\rho}_i) \times \dot{\bar{\mathbf{r}}} + \Sigma \boldsymbol{\rho}_i \times m_i \dot{\boldsymbol{\rho}}_i.$$

Now by (5) the second and third terms on the right-hand side vanish so that

$$\Sigma \mathbf{r}_i \times m_i \dot{\mathbf{r}}_i = \bar{\mathbf{r}} \times M\dot{\bar{\mathbf{r}}} + \Sigma \boldsymbol{\rho}_i \times m_i \dot{\boldsymbol{\rho}}_i,$$

or
$$\mathbf{h}_O = \bar{\mathbf{r}} \times M\dot{\bar{\mathbf{r}}} + \mathbf{h}_Q, \qquad . \qquad . \qquad . \quad (13)$$

where $\mathbf{h}_Q$ is the resultant moment of momentum about the mass centre. This states that *the moment of momentum about any fixed point O is equal to the moment of momentum about O of a particle of mass equal to the total mass of the system placed at and moving with the mass centre together with the moment of momentum about the mass centre.* Combining (11), (12) and (13), we have

$$\mathbf{G}_Q + \bar{\mathbf{r}} \times \mathbf{F} = \bar{\mathbf{r}} \times M\ddot{\bar{\mathbf{r}}} + \dot{\mathbf{h}}_Q.$$

Applying (9) this yields the result which we set out to prove
$$\mathbf{G}_Q = \dot{\mathbf{h}}_Q. \qquad . \qquad . \qquad . \qquad . \quad (14)$$

§ 35. The **kinetic energy** of a particle of mass m and velocity $\dot{\mathbf{r}}$ is defined to be $\frac{1}{2}m\dot{\mathbf{r}} \cdot \dot{\mathbf{r}}$. It follows that the kinetic energy T of a system of particles is $\frac{1}{2}\Sigma m_i \dot{\mathbf{r}}_i \cdot \dot{\mathbf{r}}_i$. With the same notation as in § 34 we have

$$2T = \Sigma m_i \dot{\mathbf{r}}_i \cdot \dot{\mathbf{r}}_i = \Sigma m_i (\dot{\bar{\mathbf{r}}} + \dot{\boldsymbol{\rho}}_i) \cdot (\dot{\bar{\mathbf{r}}} + \dot{\boldsymbol{\rho}}_i)$$
$$= M\dot{\bar{\mathbf{r}}} \cdot \dot{\bar{\mathbf{r}}} + 2(\Sigma m_i \dot{\boldsymbol{\rho}}_i) \cdot \dot{\bar{\mathbf{r}}} + \Sigma m_i \dot{\boldsymbol{\rho}}_i \cdot \dot{\boldsymbol{\rho}}_i.$$

The middle term vanishes as before so that

$$2T = M\dot{\bar{\mathbf{r}}} \cdot \dot{\bar{\mathbf{r}}} + \Sigma m_i \dot{\boldsymbol{\rho}}_i \cdot \dot{\boldsymbol{\rho}}_i. \qquad . \qquad . \qquad . \quad (15)$$

Hence *the kinetic energy of a system of particles is equal to the kinetic energy of a mass equal to the total mass of the system placed at and moving with the mass centre together with the kinetic energy of the system relative to the mass centre.*

§ 36. So far we have only dealt with systems of particles. Before we can apply our results to rigid bodies we must make an additional assumption of some sort. The assumption we shall make is known as **Boscovitch's hypothesis** which may be stated in the form : *So far as the motion of a rigid body is concerned it may be treated as though it consisted of a system of material particles rigidly connected together.* This hypothesis enables us to apply the formulae (9), (11), (13), (14) and (15) to rigid bodies as well as to systems of particles but it should be observed that when dealing with rigid bodies we must replace summations by integrations. In particular $M = \int dm$, $M\bar{\mathbf{r}} = \int \mathbf{r} dm$. In §§ 40-42 we shall show how expressions of the type $\int \mathbf{r} \times \dot{\mathbf{r}} dm$ and $\frac{1}{2}\int \dot{\mathbf{r}} \cdot \dot{\mathbf{r}} dm$ may be evaluated.

Now the position in space of any rigid body is determined when we know the coordinates of each of three non-collinear points of the body. These nine quantities are not independent but are connected by the three relations which state that the lengths of the lines joining the three points are invariable. It follows that the position of a rigid body is determined by six independent quantities.

To determine these six independent quantities we require six independent scalar equations. These are supplied either by (10) and (11)

$$\mathbf{F} = \dot{\mathbf{p}}, \quad \mathbf{G}_O = \dot{\mathbf{h}}_O,$$

or by (10) and (14)

$$\mathbf{F} = \dot{\mathbf{p}}, \quad \mathbf{G}_Q = \dot{\mathbf{h}}_Q.$$

In either case the first equation determines the motion of the mass centre and the second determines the rotational motion of the body.

§ **37.** Finite rotations about different axes, although they can be represented by straight lines in magnitude and direction, are not commutative and may not be added according to the vector law. Infinitesimal rotations on the other hand may be represented by vectors as we shall now show.

Consider an infinitesimal rotation through an angle $\delta\theta$ about an axis through the origin specified by the unit vector $\mathbf{e}$. A point whose position vector was originally $\mathbf{r}$ will take up a new position $\mathbf{r} + \delta\mathbf{r}$ and it will be seen that $\delta\mathbf{r}$ is perpendicular to both $\mathbf{e}$ and $\mathbf{r}$. The point will move through a distance $r \sin \phi \, \delta\theta$ where ϕ is the angle between $\mathbf{e}$ and $\mathbf{r}$. This follows since the radius of the infinitesimal arc of the circle along which the point moves is $r \sin \phi$.

From these facts we conclude that

$$\delta\mathbf{r} = \delta\theta\mathbf{e} \times \mathbf{r},$$

and that $\qquad \dot{\mathbf{r}} = \lim_{\delta t \to 0} \frac{\delta\mathbf{r}}{\delta t} = \dot{\theta}\mathbf{e} \times \mathbf{r} = \boldsymbol{\omega} \times \mathbf{r},$ . . . (16)

where $\boldsymbol{\omega}$ denotes the vector $\dot{\theta}\mathbf{e}$.

We have seen that if a point $\mathbf{r}$ is subjected to an infinitesimal rotation $\delta\theta_1$ about an axis $\mathbf{e}_1$ the point will take up a new position

$$\mathbf{r}_1 = \mathbf{r} + \delta\theta_1\mathbf{e}_1 \times \mathbf{r}.$$

If this rotation is followed by another infinitesimal rotation $\delta\theta_2$ about an axis $\mathbf{e}_2$ through O, the new position of the point is given by

$$\mathbf{r}_{12} = (\mathbf{r} + \delta\theta_1\mathbf{e}_1 \times \mathbf{r}) + \delta\theta_2\mathbf{e}_2 \times (\mathbf{r} + \delta\theta_1\mathbf{e}_1 \times \mathbf{r}).$$

Neglecting $\delta\theta_2\delta\theta_1$, we deduce that

$$\mathbf{r}_{12} = \mathbf{r} + (\delta\theta_1\mathbf{e}_1 + \delta\theta_2\mathbf{e}_2) \times \mathbf{r} = \mathbf{r}_{21},$$

showing that infinitesimal rotations are commutative. The same is true for angular velocities, in fact

$$\dot{\mathbf{r}} = \lim_{\delta t \to 0} \frac{\mathbf{r}_{12} - \mathbf{r}}{\delta t} = (\dot{\theta}_1\mathbf{e}_1 + \dot{\theta}_2\mathbf{e}_2) \times \mathbf{r}.$$

If we now represent the angular velocity $\dot{\theta}_1\mathbf{e}_1$ by a vector $\boldsymbol{\omega}_1$ and $\dot{\theta}_2\mathbf{e}_2$ by a vector $\boldsymbol{\omega}_2$, we have

$$\dot{\mathbf{r}} = (\boldsymbol{\omega}_1 + \boldsymbol{\omega}_2) \times \mathbf{r},$$

which is equivalent to the effect produced by a single angular velocity $\boldsymbol{\omega}_1 + \boldsymbol{\omega}_2$. We conclude that angular velocities are added according to the vector law and may be resolved into components in the usual way.

§ 38. Let $OXYZ$ be a set of rectangular axes fixed in space and let $OX'Y'Z'$ be another set momentarily coincident with $OXYZ$ but rotating about O with angular velocity $\boldsymbol{\omega}$. Consider a moving point P whose position vectors relative to $OXYZ$ and $OX'Y'Z'$ are $\mathbf{r}$ and $\mathbf{r}'$ respectively. At the instant, which we may call $t = 0$ when $OXYZ$ and $OX'Y'Z'$ coincide we have $\mathbf{r} = \mathbf{r}'$. It does not follow, however, that $\dot{\mathbf{r}}$ and $\dot{\mathbf{r}}'$ are the same, as we shall presently see. At time δt the point P has moved to a new position $\mathbf{r} + \delta \mathbf{r}$ relative to $OXYZ$ and to a new position $\mathbf{r}' + \delta \mathbf{r}'$ relative to $OX'Y'Z'$ but, owing to the motion of $OX'Y'Z'$, $\mathbf{r}'$ no longer coincides with $\mathbf{r}$. An argument similar to that of § 37 shows that at time δt

$$\mathbf{r}' = \mathbf{r} + \boldsymbol{\omega} \times \mathbf{r}' \delta t.$$

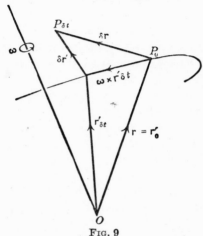

Fig. 9

As will be seen from fig. 9 we now have

$$\delta \mathbf{r} = \delta \mathbf{r}' + \boldsymbol{\omega} \times \mathbf{r}' \delta t,$$

whence $\quad\quad\quad\quad \dot{\mathbf{r}} = \dot{\mathbf{r}}' + \boldsymbol{\omega} \times \mathbf{r}'.$

A similar argument holds for any vector $\mathbf{a}$ and the rate of change of $\mathbf{a}$ with respect to axes fixed in space is

$$\dot{\mathbf{a}} = \dot{\mathbf{a}}' + \boldsymbol{\omega} \times \mathbf{a}'. \quad . \quad\quad . \quad\quad . \quad\quad . \quad (17)$$

§ 39. Using the value of $\dot{\mathbf{r}}$ given in the formula

$$\dot{\mathbf{r}} = \dot{\mathbf{r}}' + \boldsymbol{\omega} \times \mathbf{r}'$$

as $\mathbf{a}$ in (17) we have a formula for the acceleration. We find that

$$\ddot{\mathbf{r}} = \frac{d}{dt}(\dot{\mathbf{r}}' + \boldsymbol{\omega} \times \mathbf{r}') + \boldsymbol{\omega} \times (\dot{\mathbf{r}}' + \boldsymbol{\omega} \times \mathbf{r}')$$

$$= \ddot{\mathbf{r}}' + \dot{\boldsymbol{\omega}} \times \mathbf{r}' + 2\boldsymbol{\omega} \times \dot{\mathbf{r}}' + \boldsymbol{\omega} \times (\boldsymbol{\omega} \times \mathbf{r}').$$

In the two-dimensional case $(z' = \omega_x = \omega_y = 0)$ the components of the velocity $\dot{\mathbf{r}}$ in the directions of the moving axes OX' and OY' are

$$\dot{x}' - y'\omega, \quad \dot{y}' + x'\omega,$$

and those of the acceleration $\ddot{\mathbf{r}}$ are

$$\ddot{x}' - y'\dot{\omega} - 2\dot{y}'\omega - x'\omega^2, \quad \ddot{y}' + x'\dot{\omega} + 2\dot{x}'\omega - y'\omega^2.$$

If we now take OX' to be the direction of $\mathbf{r}$, we at once obtain the radial and transverse components of velocity and acceleration by putting $y' = \dot{y}' = \ddot{y}' = 0$, $x' = r$. The radial and transverse components of the velocity are evidently

$$\dot{r} \quad \text{and} \quad r\omega$$

respectively, while those of the acceleration are

$$\ddot{r} - r\omega^2 \quad \text{and} \quad r\dot{\omega} + 2\dot{r}\omega.$$

The transverse component of acceleration may be written in the form $\frac{1}{r}\frac{d}{dt}(r^2\omega)$. A particle which is acted upon only by a force which is always along the radius vector from a fixed point can have no transverse acceleration and so $r^2\omega$ is a constant, which we call h. Now the area δA swept out by the radius vector in time δt will be $\frac{1}{2}r^2\delta\theta$ where $\delta\theta$ is the angle swept out in time δt. The areal velocity $\frac{dA}{dt}$ is therefore $\frac{1}{2}r^2\frac{d\theta}{dt} = \frac{1}{2}r^2\omega = \frac{1}{2}h$. This in fact affords a mathematical verification of **Kepler's second law**, which states that *for a given planetary orbit, the area described by the radius drawn from the planet to the sun is proportional to the time taken.*

Again, we may express the acceleration vector in the form

$$\dot{\mathbf{v}} + \boldsymbol{\omega} \times \mathbf{v},$$

E

where **v** is the velocity relative to the moving axes. If we choose OX' to be in the direction of **v** we see that the tangential and normal components of the acceleration are

$$\dot{v} \quad \text{and} \quad v\omega$$

respectively. Now in this case

$$\omega = \frac{d\psi}{dt} = \frac{d\psi}{dl}\frac{dl}{dt} = \frac{v}{\rho}$$

where ψ is the angle which the tangent makes with OX and ρ is the radius of curvature. (The formula $\rho = dl/d\psi$ is given in textbooks on the differential calculus.) We conclude that the normal component of acceleration in the direction OY' is v^2/ρ.

Lastly, in the two-dimensional case with constant angular velocity the components of acceleration relative to fixed axes coinciding instantaneously with the moving axes are

$$\ddot{x}' - 2\dot{y}'\omega - x'\omega^2, \quad \ddot{y}' + 2\dot{x}'\omega - y'\omega^2.$$

If F_x and F_y be the components in these directions of the force on the particle of mass m at P, then Newton's Law gives

$$m\ddot{x}' = F_x + 2m\dot{y}'\omega + mx'\omega^2,$$
$$m\ddot{y}' = F_y - 2m\dot{x}'\omega + my'\omega^2.$$

If an observer assumes mistakenly or willingly that the moving axes $OX'Y'$ are at rest, that is to say, if he assumes that $\ddot{x}'$ and $\ddot{y}'$ are the components of the acceleration he will not be able to account for the motion of the particle unless he invents the following fictitious forces acting on the particle : (i) the **centrifugal force** with components $mx'\omega^2$ and $my'\omega^2$ which is a force of magnitude $mr\omega^2$ acting outwards along the radius vector ; (ii) the **Coriolis force** with components $+2m\dot{y}'\omega$ and $-2m\dot{x}'\omega$. The Coriolis force vanishes if the particle is at rest relative to the moving axes.

§ 40. Consider now the case of a rigid body rotating about a fixed point which we choose to be the origin with an angular velocity $\boldsymbol{\omega}$. We have seen in § 37 that the velocity $\dot{\mathbf{r}}$ of the point $\mathbf{r}$ is $\boldsymbol{\omega} \times \mathbf{r}$. Substituting this value in the formula for the moment of momentum vector about O, we find that

$$\mathbf{h} = \int \mathbf{r} \times \dot{\mathbf{r}} \, dm = \int \mathbf{r} \times (\boldsymbol{\omega} \times \mathbf{r}) dm = \int (\mathbf{r} \cdot \mathbf{r}) \boldsymbol{\omega} \, dm - \int (\mathbf{r} \cdot \boldsymbol{\omega}) \mathbf{r} \, dm.$$

We readily verify that

$$h_x = \left[\int (y^2 + z^2) dm \right] \omega_x - \left[\int xy \, dm \right] \omega_y - \left[\int xz \, dm \right] \omega_z.$$

Writing

$$A \equiv \int (y^2 + z^2) dm, \quad B \equiv \int (z^2 + x^2) dm, \quad C \equiv \int (x^2 + y^2) dm,$$

$$D \equiv \int yz \, dm, \qquad E \equiv \int zx \, dm, \qquad F \equiv \int xy \, dm,$$

we have

$$h_x = + A \omega_x - F \omega_y - E \omega_z, \quad h_y = - F \omega_x + B \omega_y - D \omega_z,$$
$$h_z = - E \omega_x - D \omega_y + C \omega_z,$$

or in matrix notation

$$\begin{bmatrix} h_x \\ h_y \\ h_z \end{bmatrix} = \begin{bmatrix} +A & -F & -E \\ -F & +B & -D \\ -E & -D & +C \end{bmatrix} \begin{bmatrix} \omega_x \\ \omega_y \\ \omega_z \end{bmatrix}.$$

The quantities A, B, C are called the moments of inertia of the body about the coordinate axes OX, OY, OZ and D, E, F are called the products of inertia about the same axes.

Since the body is moving relative to the fixed axes $OXYZ$, the moments and products of inertia about these axes are continually changing with the time and their rates of change enter into the formulae

$$G_x = \dot{h}_x = d(+ A \omega_x - F \omega_y - E \omega_z) / dt,$$
$$G_y = \dot{h}_y = d(- F \omega +_x B \omega_y - D \omega_z) / dt,$$
$$G_z = \dot{h}_z = d(- E \omega_x - D \omega_y + C \omega_z) / dt.$$

To avoid this difficulty we choose moving axes $OX'Y'Z'$

fixed in the body and momentarily coinciding with $OXYZ$. In accordance with (17) we have

$$G_x = d(A\omega_x - F\omega_y - E\omega_z)/dt + \omega_y(-E\omega_x - D\omega_y + C\omega_z)$$
$$- \omega_z(-F\omega_x + B\omega_y - D\omega_z)$$

and two other equations like it. In this formula the moments and products of inertia are with respect to axes fixed in the body. These are constants of the body and can be evaluated by integration. If we choose the principal axes of inertia at O (see § 41) as the moving axes $OX'Y'Z'$ then the equations of motion become

$$G_x = A^*\dot{\omega}_x + (C^* - B^*)\omega_y\omega_z,$$
$$G_y = B^*\dot{\omega}_y + (A^* - C^*)\omega_z\omega_x,$$
$$G_z = C^*\dot{\omega}_z + (B^* - A^*)\omega_x\omega_y.$$

These are **Euler's equations of motion**. In the above formulae G_x, G_y, G_z and ω_x, ω_y, ω_z denote components of **G** and **ω** about the principal axes of inertia at O.

The foregoing arguments apply to the motion of a rigid body about a fixed point O. Exactly similar arguments can be constructed for the motion of a rigid body about its mass centre Q if the corresponding modifications are made of the meanings attached to the symbols employed.

§ **41.** The reader who is familiar with the theory of matrices will appreciate the following method of evaluating the moments and products of inertia about any set of rectangular axes $OX'Y'Z'$ through an origin O when they are known about a given set of axes $OXYZ$ with the same origin O. We write

$$\mathsf{H} = \begin{vmatrix} +A & -F & -E \\ -F & +B & -D \\ -E & -D & +C \end{vmatrix}, \qquad \mathsf{H}' = \begin{vmatrix} +A' & -F' & -E' \\ -F' & +B' & -D' \\ -E' & -D' & +C' \end{vmatrix},$$

$$\mathbf{r} = \begin{vmatrix} x \\ y \\ z \end{vmatrix}, \qquad \mathbf{r}' = \begin{vmatrix} x' \\ y' \\ z' \end{vmatrix}.$$

As we are using a dash to denote quantities associated with the axes $OX'Y'Z'$, we shall use a superscript T to denote transposed matrices and vectors. We observe that

$$\mathsf{H} = k\,\mathsf{I} - \int \mathbf{r}\,\mathbf{r}^T\,dm, \quad k = \int \mathbf{r}^T\,\mathbf{r}\,dm,$$

$$\mathsf{H}' = k'\mathsf{I} - \int \mathbf{r}'\mathbf{r}'^T dm, \quad k' = \int \mathbf{r}'^T\mathbf{r}'dm,$$

where I denotes the unit matrix. Now since the transformation from $OXYZ$ to $OX'Y'Z'$ is an orthogonal one, we have

$$\mathbf{r}' = \mathsf{P}\mathbf{r}, \quad \mathbf{r}'^T = \mathbf{r}^T\mathsf{P}^T, \quad \mathsf{P}\mathsf{P}^T = \mathsf{P}^T\mathsf{P} = \mathsf{I}.$$

It follows that

$$k' = \int \mathbf{r}'^T\mathbf{r}'dm = \int \mathbf{r}^T\mathsf{P}^T\mathsf{P}\mathbf{r}dm = \int \mathbf{r}^T\mathbf{r}dm = k.$$

So

$$\mathsf{H}' = k\mathsf{I} - \mathsf{P}\Big(\int \mathbf{r}\mathbf{r}^Tdm\Big)\mathsf{P}^T = \mathsf{P}\Big(k\mathsf{I} - \int \mathbf{r}\mathbf{r}^Tdm\Big)\mathsf{P}^T = \mathsf{P}\mathsf{H}\mathsf{P}^T.$$

Hence, if

$$x' = \lambda_1 x + \mu_1 y + \nu_1 z,$$
$$y' = \lambda_2 x + \mu_2 y + \nu_2 z,$$
$$z' = \lambda_3 x + \mu_3 y + \nu_3 z,$$

then

$$\begin{vmatrix} +A' & -F' & -E' \\ -F' & +B' & -D' \\ -E' & -D' & +C' \end{vmatrix} = \begin{vmatrix} \lambda_1 & \mu_1 & \nu_1 \\ \lambda_2 & \mu_2 & \nu_2 \\ \lambda_3 & \mu_3 & \nu_3 \end{vmatrix} \begin{vmatrix} +A & -F & -E \\ -F & +B & -D \\ -E & -D & +C \end{vmatrix} \begin{vmatrix} \lambda_1 & \lambda_2 & \lambda_3 \\ \mu_1 & \mu_2 & \mu_3 \\ \nu_1 & \nu_2 & \nu_3 \end{vmatrix}.$$

Thus

$$A' = \lambda_1{}^2 A + \mu_1{}^2 B + \nu_1{}^2 C - 2\mu_1\nu_1 D - 2\nu_1\lambda_1 E - 2\lambda_1\mu_1 F,$$
$$D' = -\lambda_2\lambda_3 A - \mu_2\mu_3 B - \nu_2\nu_3 C + (\mu_2\nu_3 + \nu_2\mu_3)D$$
$$+ (\nu_2\lambda_3 + \lambda_2\nu_3)E + (\lambda_2\mu_3 + \mu_2\lambda_3)F,$$

and similar relations hold for B', C', E', F'. Now for any symmetric matrix H it is always possible* to find an

* Aitken, *Determinants and Matrices*, p. 89, Ex. 9.

orthogonal matrix P such that PHP^T takes the diagonal form

$$\begin{vmatrix} A^* & 0 & 0 \\ 0 & B^* & 0 \\ 0 & 0 & C^* \end{vmatrix}$$

The coordinate axes $OX^*Y^*Z^*$ thus defined are the **principal axes of inertia** of the body at the given point O and A^*, B^*, C^* are the **principal moments of inertia** at this point O.

§ **42.** If T be the kinetic energy of a rigid body which is rotating about a fixed point O with angular velocity $\boldsymbol{\omega}$, then

$$\begin{aligned} T &= \tfrac{1}{2}\int \dot{\mathbf{r}} \cdot \dot{\mathbf{r}}\,dm \\ &= \tfrac{1}{2}\int (\boldsymbol{\omega} \times \mathbf{r}) \cdot (\boldsymbol{\omega} \times \mathbf{r})\,dm \\ &= \tfrac{1}{2}\int [\boldsymbol{\omega}, \mathbf{r}, \boldsymbol{\omega} \times \mathbf{r}]\,dm \\ &= \tfrac{1}{2}\int \boldsymbol{\omega} \cdot \mathbf{r} \times (\boldsymbol{\omega} \times \mathbf{r})\,dm \\ &= \tfrac{1}{2}\boldsymbol{\omega} \cdot \int \mathbf{r} \times (\boldsymbol{\omega} \times \mathbf{r})\,dm \\ &= \tfrac{1}{2}\boldsymbol{\omega} \cdot \mathbf{h}. \end{aligned}$$

Substituting the values for h_x, h_y, h_z found in § 40, we obtain

$$\begin{aligned} T &= \tfrac{1}{2}(A\omega^2_x + B\omega^2_y + C\omega^2_z - 2D\omega_y\omega_z - 2E\omega_z\omega_x - 2F\omega_x\omega_y) \\ &= \tfrac{1}{2}\omega^2(A\lambda^2 + B\mu^2 + C\nu^2 - 2D\mu\nu - 2E\nu\lambda - 2F\lambda\mu) \\ &= \tfrac{1}{2}\omega^2 I, \end{aligned}$$

where λ, μ, ν are the direction cosines of $\boldsymbol{\omega}$ and I is the moment of inertia of the body about the instantaneous axis of rotation. If θ be the angle between $\boldsymbol{\omega}$ and $\mathbf{h}$, then $T = \tfrac{1}{2}\omega h \cos \theta$ so that

$$h = \omega I \sec \theta.$$

In the two-dimensional case $\boldsymbol{\omega}$ and $\mathbf{h}$ are always parallel, from which we deduce the useful formula

$$h = \omega I.$$

The foregoing arguments apply to the motion of a rigid body about a fixed point O. Exactly similar arguments can be constructed for the motion of a rigid body about its mass centre Q if the corresponding modifications are made of the meanings attached to the symbols employed.

§ 43. A force is said to do work when its point of application moves. If a force $\mathbf{F}$ is applied to a particle and the particle moves a small distance $\delta \mathbf{l}$, the **work** done by $\mathbf{F}$ in this displacement is defined to be

$$\mathbf{F} . \delta \mathbf{l}.$$

It should be noted that $\mathbf{F} . \delta \mathbf{l}$ is the work done by $\mathbf{F}$ whether or not other forces are acting on the particle. It may happen that the other forces make the particle move in a direction directly opposite to that of $\mathbf{F}$ in which case $\mathbf{F} . \delta \mathbf{l}$ will be a negative quantity.

If a system of forces $\mathbf{F}_1$, $\mathbf{F}_2$, ... act on a particle and the particle suffers a displacement $\delta \mathbf{l}$, then the total work done on the particle by the different forces is

$$\mathbf{F}_1 . \delta \mathbf{l} + \mathbf{F}_2 . \delta \mathbf{l} + \ldots . = (\mathbf{F}_1 + \mathbf{F}_2 + \ldots .) . \delta \mathbf{l}$$
$$= (\Sigma \mathbf{F}_i) . \delta \mathbf{l}.$$

Hence if the system of forces be in equilibrium, then $\Sigma \mathbf{F}_i = \mathbf{0}$ and the total work done is zero. This leads to the principle of **virtual work** for a particle ; viz., *if a particle is in equilibrium under a system of forces then the total work done by these forces in any infinitesimal displacement of the particle is zero.* It can be shown that the principle holds good even when applied to a system of rigid bodies.

§ 44. When a particle subject to given forces undergoes a finite displacement, the total work done is found by integrating the amounts done on it in traversing the various elements $d\mathbf{l}$ of its path. The particle is said to move in a **field of force**. The work done by a **variable force** $\mathbf{F}$ when the particle moves from $\mathbf{r}_1$ to $\mathbf{r}_2$ is *

$$\int_{\mathbf{r}_1}^{\mathbf{r}_2} \mathbf{F} . d\mathbf{l}.$$

* Integrals of this type are explained in § 48.

Certain fields of force have the property that the work done by the forces of the field in a displacement of a particle from one point to another depends only on the initial and final positions of the particle, being the same whatever the sequence of infinitesimal displacements by which the finite displacement is effected. Fields of force of this type are called **conservative**. The gravitational forces of attraction and elastic forces are examples of conservative forces but friction is a non-conservative force.

The **potential energy** V at any point $\mathbf{r}$ is the work done by the conservative forces of the field when the particle moves from its position $\mathbf{r}$ to some standard position $\mathbf{r_0}$. Thus if $\mathbf{F}$ represents the resultant conservative force acting on the particle the potential energy of the particle when at $\mathbf{r}$ is

$$V = \int_{\mathbf{r}}^{\mathbf{r_0}} \mathbf{F} \cdot d\mathbf{l}.$$

It will be noticed that since $\mathbf{F}$ is conservative, V is a function of x, y, z the coordinates of the particle. V is a function of position and to denote this we write

$$V = V(x, y, z).$$

Points with the same potential energy will lie on the surface

$$V(x, y, z) = \text{constant}.$$

The work done by the conservative forces when the particle moves from $\mathbf{r_1}$ to $\mathbf{r_2}$ is

$$\int_{\mathbf{r_1}}^{\mathbf{r_2}} \mathbf{F} \cdot d\mathbf{l},$$

and since this does not depend upon the path joining $\mathbf{r_1}$ to $\mathbf{r_2}$ we may choose a path passing through $\mathbf{r_0}$. The work done may now be expressed as

$$\int_{\mathbf{r_1}}^{\mathbf{r_0}} \mathbf{F} \cdot d\mathbf{l} + \int_{\mathbf{r_0}}^{\mathbf{r_2}} \mathbf{F} \cdot d\mathbf{l},$$

or $V(x_1, y_1, z_1) - V(x_2, y_2, z_2).$

Thus the work done is the decrease in potential energy.

In particular, choose $x_2 = x_1 + \delta x$, $y_2 = y_1 + \delta y$, $z_2 = z_1 + \delta z$ and write $V_2 = V_1 + \delta V$; then $\mathbf{F} \cdot d\mathbf{l} = F_x \delta x + F_y \delta y + F_z \delta z$ and the work done is

$$\int_{\mathbf{r}_1}^{\mathbf{r}_2} F_x dx + F_y dy + F_z dz = F_x \delta x + F_y \delta y + F_z \delta z = -\delta V.$$

Hence

$$F_x = -\frac{\partial V}{\partial x}, \quad F_y = -\frac{\partial V}{\partial y}, \quad F_z = -\frac{\partial V}{\partial z},$$

and so

$$\mathbf{F} = -\frac{\partial V}{\partial x}\mathbf{i} - \frac{\partial V}{\partial y}\mathbf{j} - \frac{\partial V}{\partial z}\mathbf{k}.$$

We shall discuss vectors of this type in more detail in § 47.

The work done in a small displacement is $-\delta V$ and by the virtual work principle this must be zero if the forces are in equilibrium. We may therefore state that the condition for the equilibrium of a particle is that the potential energy have a stationary value. This theorem may also be applied to a rigid body.

§ 45. We consider now a single particle of mass m under the action of conservative forces only. As it moves from the point $\mathbf{r}$ to the point $\mathbf{r} + \delta\mathbf{r}$, it moves through a small distance $\delta\mathbf{r}$ and the work done by the conservative forces is $\mathbf{F} \cdot \delta\mathbf{r}$ or $-\delta V$, where V is the potential energy. Its kinetic energy is increased by an amount

$$\delta T = \delta(\tfrac{1}{2}m\dot{\mathbf{r}} \cdot \dot{\mathbf{r}}) = \frac{d}{dt}(\tfrac{1}{2}m\dot{\mathbf{r}} \cdot \dot{\mathbf{r}})\delta t = m\ddot{\mathbf{r}} \cdot \dot{\mathbf{r}}\delta t = \mathbf{F} \cdot \delta\mathbf{r} = -\delta V.$$

Thus for a particle moving under conservative forces $\delta(T + V) = 0$; that is to say,

$$T + V = \text{constant}.$$

This is the theorem of conservation of mechanical energy for a single particle. Since it is true for each particle of a system of particles, it must also be true for a system of particles provided that all the forces between the particles are conservative ones. Now we may assume according to

Boscovitch's hypothesis that a rigid body is composed of particles rigidly connected together. This means that the distance between the ith and jth particles is constant, or that

$$(\mathbf{r}_i - \mathbf{r}_j)^2 = \text{constant}.$$

Hence $(\mathbf{r}_i - \mathbf{r}_j) \cdot (\delta\mathbf{r}_i - \delta\mathbf{r}_j) = 0$. But since $\mathbf{F}_{ij} = \lambda_{ij}(\mathbf{r}_i - \mathbf{r}_j)$, we deduce that $\mathbf{F}_{ij} \cdot (\delta\mathbf{r}_i - \delta\mathbf{r}_j) = 0$. It follows that

$$\mathbf{F}_{ij} \cdot \delta\mathbf{r}_i = \mathbf{F}_{ij} \cdot \delta\mathbf{r}_j = -\mathbf{F}_{ji} \cdot \delta\mathbf{r}_j.$$

From this we conclude that during the motion of a rigid body no work is done by the internal forces and that no change in the total potential energy results from the internal forces whether or not these forces are conservative. This is in fact **D'Alembert's principle**. It follows at once that the theorem of conservation of mechanical energy holds good in the case of rigid bodies provided that all the external forces are conservative.

A careful distinction must be made between this theorem and the physical principle of conservation of energy by which energy cannot be destroyed but can only be converted from one form to another. This distinction helps us to comprehend the nature of conservative forces. When conservative forces only are acting, kinetic and potential energy may be converted into one another but neither can be transformed into any other sort such as electrical energy or heat. Friction must be a non-conservative force since it gives rise to heat and sound.

§ 46. Examples

(1) Two forces of magnitudes P and Q act respectively in two straight lines the shortest distance between which is r and whose directions are inclined at an angle θ. Show that the pitch of the equivalent wrench is

$$\frac{PQr \sin \theta}{P^2 + Q^2 + 2PQ \cos \theta}.$$

(2) The directions of two non-intersecting forces, whose magnitudes are P and Q, are perpendicular. Show that the distances of the central axis from their lines of action are in the ratio $Q^2 : P^2$.

(3) A force of magnitude P acts parallel to OX through the point $(0, 0, 1)$. A second force of magnitude $3P$ acts along a line through the point $(1, 0, 0)$ with direction cosines $0, \frac{3}{5}, \frac{4}{5}$. Show that the pitch of the equivalent wrench is $0 \cdot 18$.

(4) By solving the equations

$$\ddot{r} - r\omega^2 = 0, \quad 2\dot{r}\omega + r\dot{\omega} = 0,$$

show that there is uniform motion in a straight line if there is no radial or transverse acceleration.

(5) If the tangential and normal components of the acceleration of a particle moving in a plane are both constant, show that the particle describes a logarithmic spiral.

(6) A particle P moves in a plane with constant angular velocity ω about O. If the rate of increase of its acceleration is parallel to OP, prove that $\dddot{r} = \frac{1}{3}r\omega^2$.

(7) A thin rod OP whose end O is fixed is rotated in a horizontal circle with constant angular velocity ω. A bead of mass m is free to slide on the rod and is initially at rest relative to the rod at distance a from O. Show that the horizontal pressure of the rod on the bead is $2m\omega^2\sqrt{(x^2 - a^2)}$ where x is the distance of the bead from O.

(8) Find the potential energy of a particle acted on by an elastic force $-kr$ where k is a constant. (Choose the origin as the standard position.) $[\frac{1}{2}kr^2.]$

(9) Find the potential energy of a particle acted on by an inverse square force $\dfrac{-k}{r^3}\mathbf{r}$ where k is a constant. (Choose $r = a$ as the standard position.) $[k\left(\dfrac{1}{a} - \dfrac{1}{r}\right).]$

(10) Prove that if the resultant moment $\mathbf{G}$ of the external forces about a fixed point O is perpendicular to the angular velocity $\boldsymbol{\omega}$ of a rigid body which is rotating about O, then the kinetic energy T of the body is constant.

Show also that if $\mathbf{G}$ is perpendicular to the moment of momentum $\mathbf{h}$ about O, then h is constant.

CHAPTER IV

THE VECTOR OPERATOR "∇"

§ 47. THE equation $\phi(x, y, z) = C$ represents a surface in three-dimensional space. If we vary the value of C we obtain a family of surfaces. One surface of this family will pass through any point (x, y, z). It is shown in textbooks on coordinate geometry that the direction cosines of the normal at (x, y, z) to the surface through that point are proportional to $\dfrac{\partial \phi}{\partial x}, \dfrac{\partial \phi}{\partial y}, \dfrac{\partial \phi}{\partial z}$. The vector

$$\frac{\partial \phi}{\partial x}\mathbf{i} + \frac{\partial \phi}{\partial y}\mathbf{j} + \frac{\partial \phi}{\partial z}\mathbf{k} \quad . \quad \quad \quad \quad (1)$$

is therefore a vector in the same direction as the normal to the surface at (x, y, z). Let dn be the element of length in this direction ; then the direction cosines of the normal are $\dfrac{dx}{dn}, \dfrac{dy}{dn}, \dfrac{dz}{dn}$ and the magnitude of the vector (1) is

$$\frac{\partial \phi}{\partial x}\frac{dx}{dn} + \frac{\partial \phi}{\partial y}\frac{dy}{dn} + \frac{\partial \phi}{\partial z}\frac{dz}{dn} = \frac{\partial \phi}{\partial n},$$

where $\dfrac{\partial}{\partial n}$ represents differentiation along the normal. In other words the magnitude of the vector (1) is the rate of change of ϕ as we move along the normal to the surface. The vector (1) is called the **gradient** of ϕ (written grad ϕ).

A convenient method of writing grad ϕ is $\nabla \phi$, where ∇ (pronounced " nabla ") is defined as the **vector operator**

$$\nabla \equiv \mathbf{i}\frac{\partial}{\partial x} + \mathbf{j}\frac{\partial}{\partial y} + \mathbf{k}\frac{\partial}{\partial z}. \quad . \quad \quad \quad (2)$$

We observe that

$$\nabla(\theta + \phi) = \nabla\theta + \nabla\phi$$

and $$\nabla(\theta\phi) \quad = \theta(\nabla\phi) + (\nabla\theta)\phi.$$

$\nabla\phi$ is an example of a **field vector**, that is to say, $\nabla\phi$ has a definite value at each point of space but at different points it may have different values. The velocity vector of a fluid is another example of a field vector. At each point in the fluid the velocity of the fluid has a definite magnitude and direction but the velocity may be different at different points in the fluid.

§ 48. The integral

$$\int_L f(x, y, z)dl$$

is called the **curvilinear integral** * or the **line integral** of the function f along the curve L. That is to say, we evaluate $f(x, y, z)$ at the element dl of the curve L, multiply by the length dl of the element, and integrate from the beginning to the end of the curve. A two-dimensional example will make this clear. We shall evaluate $\int_L (x^2 - y)dl$ where L is the smaller portion of the circle $x^2 + y^2 = a^2$ which begins at $(a, 0)$ and ends at $(0, a)$. Now for this curve $dl = ad\theta$ and $x^2 - y = a^2 \cos^2 \theta - a \sin \theta$, where θ has the usual significance. Thus

$$\int_L (x^2 - y)dl = \int_0^{\frac{1}{2}\pi} (a^2 \cos^2\theta - a \sin \theta)ad\theta = \frac{\pi}{4}a^3 - a^2.$$

In general the value of the line integral of a given function, between two points, depends upon the curve chosen between the initial and final points, but in certain important cases the value is independent of the path chosen.

If $d\mathbf{l}$ denote the vector representing an element of a

* Cf. Gillespie, *Integration* (2nd edition), p. 53.

curve, and **a** be a field vector, then

$$\mathbf{a} \cdot d\mathbf{l} = a_x dx + a_y dy + a_z dz = \left(a_x \frac{dx}{dl} + a_y \frac{dy}{dl} + a_z \frac{dz}{dl} \right) dl$$

or

$$\mathbf{a} \cdot d\mathbf{l} = (\lambda a_x + \mu a_y + \nu a_z) dl,$$

where λ, μ, ν are the direction cosines of $d\mathbf{l}$. Thus the line integral $\int_L (\lambda a_x + \mu a_y + \nu a_z) dl$ may be written

$$\int_L \mathbf{a} \cdot d\mathbf{l}$$

and is called the line integral of **a** along the curve L. If L is a curve beginning at A and ending at B, then

$$\int_{AB} \mathbf{a} \cdot d\mathbf{l} = - \int_{BA} \mathbf{a} \cdot d\mathbf{l},$$

for we alter the signs of λ, μ, ν when we reverse the direction of $d\mathbf{l}$.

§ **49.** We now wish to derive from a given field vector **a** a certain other field vector, but we shall begin with an illustration. The field vector

$$\mathbf{a} = - \omega y \mathbf{i} + \omega x \mathbf{j} + 0 \mathbf{k}$$

represents the velocity of a fluid which rotates like a rigid body with angular velocity ω about the z axis. The line integral of this vector taken round any simple closed curve in the xy plane may be shown to be $2A\omega$ where A is the area enclosed by the curve. So

$$\lim_{A \to 0} \frac{\int_L \mathbf{a} \cdot d\mathbf{l}}{A} = 2\omega.$$

If we evaluate the corresponding limit for a curve in the yz plane or the zx plane we find that it is zero. We therefore derive from the velocity vector the **vorticity** vector which in the above example has the constant value $0\mathbf{i} + 0\mathbf{j} + 2\omega\mathbf{k}$ for all points in the fluid. We now proceed to generalise.

From a field vector $\mathbf{a}$ we derive another vector called the **curl** or **rotation** of $\mathbf{a}$ (written curl $\mathbf{a}$ or rot $\mathbf{a}$) in the following manner. The component in a direction $\mathbf{n}$ of curl $\mathbf{a}$ at a point P is defined as

$$\lim_{A \to 0} \frac{\int_L \mathbf{a} \cdot d\mathbf{l}}{A},$$

where L is a simple closed curve surrounding P in the plane through P which is perpendicular to $\mathbf{n}$, where A is the area

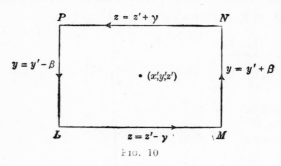

Fig. 10

enclosed by L and where the integration round L is performed in the same sense as a rotation represented by a line drawn in the direction of $\mathbf{n}$. It may be shown * that this does actually define a vector, and that the limit is independent of the shape of A.

Our next task is to obtain an analytical expression for curl $\mathbf{a}$. We shall evaluate the x component of curl $\mathbf{a}$ at a point (x', y', z') by taking A to be the area bounded by the intersection of the planes $y = y' \pm \beta$, $z = z' \pm \gamma$ with the plane $x = x'$. (See fig. 10 in which the plane of the diagram represents the plane $x = x'$.)

* Abraham, Becker, *Electricity and Magnetism*, p. 35.

By the mean value theorem

$$\int_{MN} \mathbf{a} \cdot d\mathbf{l} = \int_{-\gamma}^{+\gamma} a_z(x', y' + \beta, z)dz = 2\gamma a_z(x', y' + \beta, \zeta),$$

where $z' - \gamma \leqslant \zeta \leqslant z' + \gamma$. In the same manner

$$\int_{PL} \mathbf{a} \cdot d\mathbf{l} = -2\gamma a_z(x', y' - \beta, \zeta'); \quad z' - \gamma \leqslant \zeta' \leqslant z' + \gamma,$$

$$\int_{NP} \mathbf{a} \cdot d\mathbf{l} = -2\beta a_y(x', \eta, z' + \gamma); \quad y' - \beta \leqslant \eta \leqslant y' + \beta,$$

$$\int_{LM} \mathbf{a} \cdot d\mathbf{l} = +2\beta a_y(x', \eta', z' - \gamma); \quad y' - \beta \leqslant \eta' \leqslant y' + \beta.$$

Also $A = 4\beta\gamma$, so the x component of curl $\mathbf{a}$ is

$$\lim_{\beta \to 0} \lim_{\gamma \to 0} \frac{2\gamma\{a_z(x', y' + \beta, \zeta) - a_z(x', y' - \beta, \zeta')\}}{4\beta\gamma}$$

$$- \lim_{\gamma \to 0} \lim_{\beta \to 0} \frac{2\beta\{a_y(x', \eta, z' + \gamma) - a_y(x', \eta', z' - \gamma)\}}{4\beta\gamma}$$

$$= \lim_{\beta \to 0} \frac{a_z(x', y' + \beta, z') - a_z(x', y' - \beta, z')}{2\beta}$$

$$- \lim_{\gamma \to 0} \frac{a_y(x', y', z' + \gamma) - a_y(x', y', z' - \gamma)}{2\gamma}$$

$$= \frac{\partial}{\partial y} a_z(x', y', z') - \frac{\partial}{\partial z} a_y(x', y', z').$$

Hence

$$\text{curl } \mathbf{a} = \left(\frac{\partial a_z}{\partial y} - \frac{\partial a_y}{\partial z}\right)\mathbf{i} + \left(\frac{\partial a_x}{\partial z} - \frac{\partial a_z}{\partial x}\right)\mathbf{j} + \left(\frac{\partial a_y}{\partial x} - \frac{\partial a_x}{\partial y}\right)\mathbf{k}. \quad (3)$$

In other words,

$$\text{curl } \mathbf{a} \equiv \nabla \times \mathbf{a},$$

for by equations § 3 (8)

$$\nabla \times \mathbf{a} = \left(\mathbf{i}\frac{\partial}{\partial x} + \mathbf{j}\frac{\partial}{\partial y} + \mathbf{k}\frac{\partial}{\partial z}\right) \times (a_x\mathbf{i} + a_y\mathbf{j} + a_z\mathbf{k})$$

$$= \left(\frac{\partial a_z}{\partial y} - \frac{\partial a_y}{\partial z}\right)\mathbf{i} + \left(\frac{\partial a_x}{\partial z} - \frac{\partial a_z}{\partial x}\right)\mathbf{j} + \left(\frac{\partial a_y}{\partial x} - \frac{\partial a_x}{\partial y}\right)\mathbf{k}.$$

We observe that our definition of curl **a** is independent of our choice of coordinates, hence the expression $\nabla \times \mathbf{a}$ does not alter in form if another set of rectangular cartesian axes be chosen.

It is easily demonstrated that

$$\nabla \times (\mathbf{a} + \mathbf{b}) = \nabla \times \mathbf{a} + \nabla \times \mathbf{b}.$$

If $\nabla \times \mathbf{a} = 0$, the field vector **a** is said to be **irrotational**.

§ **50.** The integral

$$\int_S f(x, y, z) ds$$

is the **surface integral** * of the function $f(x, y, z)$ over the surface S. That is to say, we evaluate $f(x, y, z)$ at the element ds of the surface, multiply by the area ds of the element, and integrate over the surface S. The actual evaluation of such an integral will involve double integration, and some textbooks show this by writing the integral $\iint_S f(x, y, z) ds$. Except in chapter VIII, we have reserved the symbols ds and $d\mathbf{s}$ to represent elements of area so that no confusion will arise if we use only one integral sign.

As an illustration we shall evaluate $\int_S z ds$ where S is the hemisphere of $x^2 + y^2 + z^2 = a^2$ for which z is positive. Using spherical polar coordinates, we find that $z = a \cos \theta$ and $ds = a^2 \sin \theta \, d\theta d\phi$. The limits of integration for θ are 0 and $\frac{1}{2}\pi$, while those for ϕ are 0 and 2π. So

$$\int_S z ds = a^3 \int_0^{2\pi} \left(\int_0^{\frac{1}{2}\pi} \cos \theta \sin \theta \, d\theta \right) d\phi = \pi a^3.$$

A plane area may conveniently be represented by a vector whose length is numerically equal to the area, and whose direction is that of the normal to the plane. We must, however, make an arbitrary choice of the side from

---

* See Gillespie, *Integration* (2nd edition), p. 62.

F

which the vector is to be drawn. Having made such a choice, we shall refer to this side of the surface as the positive side. In the same way we may arbitrarily choose one side of a curved surface as the positive one * and then represent each element ds of the surface by a vector $d\mathbf{s}$ of magnitude ds and drawn perpendicular to the element ds on the positive side of it. We shall adopt the convention that *in the case of closed surfaces we shall always choose the outside as the positive side.*

Now

$$\mathbf{a} \cdot d\mathbf{s} = (\lambda a_x + \mu a_y + \nu a_z)ds,$$

where λ, μ, ν are the direction cosines of the normal to ds, so the surface integral $\int_S (\lambda a_x + \mu a_y + \nu a_z)ds$ may be written

$$\int_S \mathbf{a} \cdot d\mathbf{s}$$

and is called the surface integral of $\mathbf{a}$ over the surface S.

§ **51.** We now define the **divergence** of $\mathbf{a}$ (written div $\mathbf{a}$). At a point P, it is

$$\lim_{V \to 0} \frac{\int_S \mathbf{a} \cdot d\mathbf{s}}{V},$$

where S is a simple closed surface surrounding P, and V is the volume contained by S. It will be observed that no direction is associated with div $\mathbf{a}$ and that the divergence is therefore a scalar. From definition, div $\mathbf{a}$ is invariant under a change of axes. It may be shown that the limit is independent of the shape of V.

We can find an analytical expression for div $\mathbf{a}$ at $(x'y'z')$ by taking V to be the volume bounded by the planes $x = x' \pm \alpha$, $y = y' \pm \beta$, $z = z' \pm \gamma$ (fig. **11**).

By the mean value theorem $\int \mathbf{a} \cdot d\mathbf{s}$ over the face

---

* We are not concerned here with what are known as "one-sided surfaces."

$x = x' + a$, which is simply $\int a_x ds$ over this surface, is equal to $4\beta\gamma a_x(x' + a, h, k)$, where $(x' + a, h, k)$ is some point lying in this rectangular face. With a similar notation $\int \mathbf{a} \cdot d\mathbf{s}$

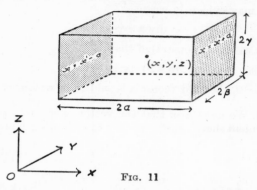

Fig. 11

over the face $x = x' - a$ is $-4\beta\gamma a_x(x' - a, h', k')$, the sign being changed since $d\mathbf{s}$ is now drawn in the opposite direction. We proceed in the same manner for the other faces. Also $V = 8a\beta\gamma$. Hence

$$\text{div } \mathbf{a} = \lim_{a \to 0} \lim_{\beta \to 0} \lim_{\gamma \to 0}$$

$$\frac{4\beta\gamma\{a_x(x' + a, h, k) - a_x(x' - a, h', k')\} + 4\gamma a\{\dots\} + 4a\beta\{\dots\}}{8a\beta\gamma}.$$

The first term is

$$\lim_{a \to 0} \left[\lim_{\beta \to 0} \lim_{\gamma \to 0} \frac{a_x(x' + a, h, k) - a_x(x' - a, h', k')}{2a} \right]$$

$$= \lim_{a \to 0} \frac{a_x(x' + a, y', z') - a_x(x' - a, y', z')}{2a}$$

$$= \frac{\partial}{\partial x} a_x(x', y', z').$$

By rearranging the order in which the limits are taken, the second and third terms are seen to be $\dfrac{\partial a_y}{\partial y}$ and $\dfrac{\partial a_z}{\partial z}$.

Hence

$$\text{div } \mathbf{a} = \frac{\partial a_x}{\partial x} + \frac{\partial a_y}{\partial y} + \frac{\partial a_z}{\partial z}, \quad \cdot \quad \cdot \quad \cdot \quad (4)$$

and we may evidently write

$$\text{div } \mathbf{a} = \nabla \cdot \mathbf{a}.$$

It is easily demonstrated that

$$\nabla \cdot (\mathbf{a} + \mathbf{b}) = \nabla \cdot \mathbf{a} + \nabla \cdot \mathbf{b}.$$

If $\nabla \cdot \mathbf{a} = 0$, the field vector $\mathbf{a}$ is said to be **solenoidal**.

§ **52.** We have seen that the vector operator ∇ provides a convenient shorthand for writing the following expressions:

$$\text{grad } \phi = \qquad \frac{\partial \phi}{\partial x}\mathbf{i} + \frac{\partial \phi}{\partial y}\mathbf{j} + \frac{\partial \phi}{\partial z}\mathbf{k} \qquad = \nabla \phi, \quad (1)$$

$$\text{curl } \mathbf{a} = \left(\frac{\partial a_z}{\partial y} - \frac{\partial a_y}{\partial z}\right)\mathbf{i} + \left(\frac{\partial a_x}{\partial z} - \frac{\partial a_z}{\partial x}\right)\mathbf{j} + \left(\frac{\partial a_y}{\partial x} - \frac{\partial a_x}{\partial y}\right)\mathbf{k} = \nabla \times \mathbf{a}, \quad (3)$$

$$\text{div } \mathbf{a} = \qquad \frac{\partial a_x}{\partial x} + \frac{\partial a_y}{\partial y} + \frac{\partial a_z}{\partial z} \qquad = \nabla \cdot \mathbf{a}. \quad (4)$$

We now establish the important identities

$$\nabla \times (\nabla \phi) = \left(\frac{\partial^2 \phi}{\partial y \partial z} - \frac{\partial^2 \phi}{\partial z \partial y}\right)\mathbf{i} + \left(\frac{\partial^2 \phi}{\partial z \partial x} - \frac{\partial^2 \phi}{\partial x \partial z}\right)\mathbf{j} + \left(\frac{\partial^2 \phi}{\partial x \partial y} - \frac{\partial^2 \phi}{\partial y \partial x}\right)\mathbf{k}$$

$$\equiv \mathbf{0}, \quad \cdot \quad \cdot \quad \cdot \quad \cdot \quad \cdot \quad \cdot \quad \cdot \quad (5)$$

$$\nabla \cdot (\nabla \times \mathbf{a}) = \frac{\partial}{\partial x}\left(\frac{\partial a_z}{\partial y} - \frac{\partial a_y}{\partial z}\right) + \frac{\partial}{\partial y}\left(\frac{\partial a_x}{\partial z} - \frac{\partial a_z}{\partial x}\right) + \frac{\partial}{\partial z}\left(\frac{\partial a_y}{\partial x} - \frac{\partial a_x}{\partial y}\right)$$

$$\equiv 0. \quad \cdot \quad \cdot \quad \cdot \quad \cdot \quad \cdot \quad \cdot \quad \cdot \quad (6)$$

Further

$$\nabla \cdot (\nabla \phi) \equiv \frac{\partial^2 \phi}{\partial x^2} + \frac{\partial^2 \phi}{\partial y^2} + \frac{\partial^2 \phi}{\partial z^2}. \quad \cdot \quad \cdot \quad (7)$$

This is an important expression which is often denoted by $\nabla^2 \phi$. Thus

$$\nabla^2 \equiv \frac{\partial^2}{\partial x^2} + \frac{\partial^2}{\partial y^2} + \frac{\partial^2}{\partial z^2}.$$

The following identities may be verified by the reader by writing both sides out in full :

$$\nabla \cdot (\phi \mathbf{a}) = \phi(\nabla \cdot \mathbf{a}) + (\nabla \phi) \cdot \mathbf{a} ; \qquad \cdot \qquad \cdot \qquad \cdot \qquad \cdot \qquad (8)$$

$$\nabla \times (\phi \mathbf{a}) = \phi(\nabla \times \mathbf{a}) + (\nabla \phi) \times \mathbf{a} ; \qquad \cdot \qquad \cdot \qquad \cdot \qquad (9)$$

$$\nabla \times (\nabla \times \mathbf{a}) = \nabla(\nabla \cdot \mathbf{a}) - \nabla^2 \mathbf{a} ; \qquad \cdot \qquad \cdot \qquad \cdot \qquad \cdot \qquad (10)$$

$$\nabla \cdot (\mathbf{a} \times \mathbf{b}) = (\nabla \times \mathbf{a}) \cdot \mathbf{b} - \mathbf{a} \cdot (\nabla \times \mathbf{b}) ; \qquad \cdot \qquad \cdot \qquad \cdot \qquad (11)$$

$$\nabla \times (\mathbf{a} \times \mathbf{b}) = \mathbf{a}(\nabla \cdot \mathbf{b}) - (\nabla \cdot \mathbf{a})\mathbf{b} + (\mathbf{b} \cdot \nabla)\mathbf{a} - (\mathbf{a} \cdot \nabla)\mathbf{b} ; \qquad (12)$$

$$\nabla(\mathbf{a} \cdot \mathbf{b}) = (\mathbf{a} \cdot \nabla)\mathbf{b} + (\mathbf{b} \cdot \nabla)\mathbf{a} + \mathbf{a} \times (\nabla \times \mathbf{b})$$
$$+ \mathbf{b} \times (\nabla \times \mathbf{a}) ; \qquad (13)$$

where $\nabla^2 \mathbf{a}$ means $(\nabla^2 a_x)\mathbf{i} + (\nabla^2 a_y)\mathbf{j} + (\nabla^2 a_z)\mathbf{k}$ and $\mathbf{a} \cdot \nabla$ is the vector operator $a_x \dfrac{\partial}{\partial x} + a_y \dfrac{\partial}{\partial y} + a_z \dfrac{\partial}{\partial z}$.

§ **53.** If we make a transformation from x, y, z to a new set of coordinates q_1, q_2, q_3, then we may write

$$x = x(q_1, q_2, q_3), \quad y = y(q_1, q_2, q_3), \quad z = z(q_1, q_2, q_3),$$

so that

$$dx = \frac{\partial x}{\partial q_1}dq_1 + \frac{\partial x}{\partial q_2}dq_2 + \frac{\partial x}{\partial q_3}dq_3,$$

and we have similar expressions for dy and dz. It follows that the element of length dl is given by

$$dl^2 = dx^2 + dy^2 + dz^2$$
$$= g_{11}dq_1{}^2 + g_{22}dq_2{}^2 + g_{33}dq_3{}^2 + 2g_{23}dq_2dq_3 + 2g_{31}dq_3dq_1$$
$$+ 2g_{12}dq_1dq_2,$$

where

$$g_{ij} = \frac{\partial x}{\partial q_i}\frac{\partial x}{\partial q_j} + \frac{\partial y}{\partial q_i}\frac{\partial y}{\partial q_j} + \frac{\partial z}{\partial q_i}\frac{\partial z}{\partial q_j} = g_{ji}.$$

Since x, y, z are independent,

$$\begin{vmatrix} \dfrac{\partial x}{\partial q_1} & \dfrac{\partial y}{\partial q_1} & \dfrac{\partial z}{\partial q_1} \\[2ex] \dfrac{\partial x}{\partial q_2} & \dfrac{\partial y}{\partial q_2} & \dfrac{\partial z}{\partial q_2} \\[2ex] \dfrac{\partial x}{\partial q_3} & \dfrac{\partial y}{\partial q_3} & \dfrac{\partial z}{\partial q_3} \end{vmatrix} \neq 0,$$

whence none of g_{11}, g_{22}, g_{33} are zero.   The element of length along a line $q_2 = $ constant, $q_3 = $ constant is $dl_1 = \sqrt{g_{11}}dq_1$. With a similar notation, $dl_2 = \sqrt{g_{22}}dq_2$ and $dl_3 = \sqrt{g_{33}}dq_3$. We shall find it convenient to write

$$h_1 = \sqrt{g_{11}}, \quad h_2 = \sqrt{g_{22}}, \quad h_3 = \sqrt{g_{33}}.$$

If we assume that the coordinates q_1, q_2, q_3 are an orthogonal system, then the element of volume must be

$$dv = h_1 h_2 h_3 dq_1 dq_2 dq_3,$$

and the element of area on the surface $q_1 = $ constant is

$$ds_1 = h_2 h_3 dq_2 dq_3.$$

The components of $\nabla\phi$ in the directions of dq_1, dq_2, dq_3 are $\dfrac{\partial\phi}{\partial l_1}$, $\dfrac{\partial\phi}{\partial l_2}$, $\dfrac{\partial\phi}{\partial l_3}$, or

$$\frac{1}{h_1}\frac{\partial\phi}{\partial q_1}, \quad \frac{1}{h_2}\frac{\partial\phi}{\partial q_2}, \quad \frac{1}{h_3}\frac{\partial\phi}{\partial q_3}. \quad \cdot \quad \cdot \quad \cdot \quad (14)$$

To obtain an expression for $\nabla \cdot \mathbf{a}$ we evaluate

$$\lim_{V \to 0} \frac{\displaystyle\int_S \mathbf{a} \cdot d\mathbf{s}}{V},$$

when S is the rectangular box bounded by the surfaces q_1, $q_1 + \delta q_1$, q_2, $q_2 + \delta q_2$, q_3, $q_3 + \delta q_3$.   Over the face q_1

$$\int \mathbf{a} \cdot d\mathbf{s} = -a_1 h_2 \delta q_2 h_3 \delta q_3,$$

where a_1, a_2, a_3 are the components of $\mathbf{a}$ in the directions of δq_1, δq_2, δq_3.   Similarly, over the face $q_1 + \delta q_1$,

$$\int \mathbf{a} \cdot d\mathbf{s} = +(a_1 h_2 \delta q_2 h_3 \delta q_3) + \frac{\partial}{\partial q_1}(a_1 h_2 \delta q_2 h_3 \delta q_3)\delta q_1.$$

Hence over these two faces together,

$$\int \mathbf{a} \cdot d\mathbf{s} = \frac{\partial}{\partial q_1}(a_1 h_2 h_3)\delta q_1 \delta q_2 \delta q_3.$$

We proceed in a similar manner for the other two pairs of faces. Thus

$$\int_S \mathbf{a} \cdot d\mathbf{s} = \left\{ \frac{\partial}{\partial q_1}(a_1 h_2 h_3) + \frac{\partial}{\partial q_2}(a_2 h_3 h_1) + \frac{\partial}{\partial q_3}(a_3 h_1 h_2) \right\} \delta q_1 \delta q_2 \delta q_3 ;$$

further $V = h_1 h_2 h_3 \delta q_1 \delta q_2 \delta q_3$, so

$$\nabla \cdot \mathbf{a} = \frac{1}{h_1 h_2 h_3} \left\{ \frac{\partial}{\partial q_1}(a_1 h_2 h_3) + \frac{\partial}{\partial q_2}(a_2 h_3 h_1) + \frac{\partial}{\partial q_3}(a_3 h_1 h_2) \right\}. \quad (15)$$

It follows from (14) and (15) that

$$\nabla^2 \phi = \frac{1}{h_1 h_2 h_3} \left\{ \frac{\partial}{\partial q_1}\left(\frac{h_2 h_3}{h_1} \frac{\partial \phi}{\partial q_1}\right) + \frac{\partial}{\partial q_2}\left(\frac{h_3 h_1}{h_2} \frac{\partial \phi}{\partial q_2}\right) + \frac{\partial}{\partial q_3}\left(\frac{h_1 h_2}{h_3} \frac{\partial \phi}{\partial q_3}\right) \right\}.$$
$$(16)$$

To obtain an expression for $\nabla \times \mathbf{a}$ we evaluate

$$\lim_{A \to 0} \frac{\int_L \mathbf{a} \cdot d\mathbf{l}}{A},$$

where A is the area lying in the surface q_1, bounded by the surfaces q_2, $q_2 + \delta q_2$, q_3, $q_3 + \delta q_3$. Along q_3

$$\int \mathbf{a} \cdot d\mathbf{l} = a_2 h_2 \delta q_2,$$

and along $q_3 + \delta q_3$

$$\int \mathbf{a} \cdot d\mathbf{l} = -(a_2 h_2 \delta q_2) - \frac{\partial}{\partial q_3}(a_2 h_2 \delta q_2)\delta q_3.$$

Hence along these two portions of L

$$\int_{\cdot} \mathbf{a} \cdot d\mathbf{l} = -\frac{\partial}{\partial q_3}(a_2 h_2)\delta q_2 \delta q_3,$$

while along the other two portions of L we find

$$\int \mathbf{a} \cdot d\mathbf{l} = +\frac{\partial}{\partial q_2}(a_3 h_3)\delta q_2 \delta q_3.$$

Now $A = h_2 h_3 \delta q_2 \delta q_3$, so the component of $\nabla \times \mathbf{a}$ in the direction of dq_1 is

$$\frac{1}{h_2 h_3} \left\{ \frac{\partial}{\partial q_2}(a_3 h_3) - \frac{\partial}{\partial q_3}(a_2 h_2) \right\} \quad . \quad \bullet \quad \bullet \quad (17)$$

Analogous expressions may be found for the other components of $\nabla \times \mathbf{a}$.

§ 54. For future reference we shall apply the formulæ of § 53 to two important cases.

(i) *Spherical polar coordinates r, θ, ψ.*
We have

$$dl^2 = dr^2 + r^2 d\theta^2 + r^2 \sin^2\theta d\psi^2,$$

so $h_1 = 1$, $h_2 = r$, $h_3 = r \sin \theta$. The components of $\nabla\phi$ are

$$\frac{\partial\phi}{\partial r}, \quad \frac{1}{r}\frac{\partial\phi}{\partial\theta}, \quad \frac{1}{r\sin\theta}\frac{\partial\phi}{\partial\psi}. \quad \bullet \quad \bullet \quad \bullet \quad (18)$$

And,

$$\nabla \cdot \mathbf{a} = \frac{1}{r^2\sin\theta}\left\{\frac{\partial}{\partial r}(a_r r^2 \sin\theta) + \frac{\partial}{\partial\theta}(a_\theta r\sin\theta) + \frac{\partial}{\partial\psi}(a_\psi r)\right\}. \quad (19)$$

$$\nabla^2\phi = \frac{1}{r^2\sin\theta}\left\{\frac{\partial}{\partial r}\left(r^2\sin\theta\frac{\partial\phi}{\partial r}\right) + \frac{\partial}{\partial\theta}\left(\sin\theta\frac{\partial\phi}{\partial\theta}\right) + \frac{\partial}{\partial\psi}\left(\frac{1}{\sin\theta}\frac{\partial\phi}{\partial\psi}\right)\right\}$$

$$= \frac{\partial^2\phi}{\partial r^2} + \frac{2}{r}\frac{\partial\phi}{\partial r} + \frac{1}{r^2}\frac{\partial^2\phi}{\partial\theta^2} + \frac{\cot\theta}{r^2}\frac{\partial\phi}{\partial\theta} + \frac{1}{r^2\sin^2\theta}\frac{\partial^2\phi}{\partial\psi^2}. \quad \bullet \quad (20)$$

The components of $\nabla \times \mathbf{a}$ are

$$\frac{1}{r^2\sin\theta}\left\{\frac{\partial}{\partial\theta}(a_\psi r\sin\theta) - \frac{\partial}{\partial\psi}(a_\theta r)\right\},$$

$$\frac{1}{r\sin\theta}\left\{\frac{\partial}{\partial\psi}(a_r) - \frac{\partial}{\partial r}(a_\psi r\sin\theta)\right\},$$

$$\frac{1}{r}\left\{\frac{\partial}{\partial r}(a_\theta r) - \frac{\partial}{\partial\theta}(a_r)\right\}. \quad \bullet \quad \bullet \quad \bullet \quad \bullet \quad (21)$$

(ii) *Cylindrical polar coordinates r, θ, z.*
We have

$$dl^2 = dr^2 + r^2 d\theta^2 + dz^2,$$

so $h_1 = 1$, $h_2 = r$, $h_3 = 1$. The components of $\nabla\phi$ are

$$\frac{\partial\phi}{\partial r}, \quad \frac{1}{r}\frac{\partial\phi}{\partial\theta}, \quad \frac{\partial\phi}{\partial z}. \quad \bullet \quad \bullet \quad \bullet \quad (22)$$

Also,

$$\nabla \cdot \mathbf{a} = \frac{1}{r}\left\{\frac{\partial}{\partial r}(a_r r) + \frac{\partial}{\partial \theta}(a_\theta) + \frac{\partial}{\partial z}(a_z r)\right\}. \qquad . \qquad (23)$$

$$\nabla^2 \phi = \frac{1}{r}\left\{\frac{\partial}{\partial r}\left(r\frac{\partial \phi}{\partial r}\right) + \frac{\partial}{\partial \theta}\left(\frac{1}{r}\frac{\partial \phi}{\partial \theta}\right) + \frac{\partial}{\partial z}\left(r\frac{\partial \phi}{\partial z}\right)\right\}$$

$$= \frac{\partial^2 \phi}{\partial r^2} + \frac{1}{r}\frac{\partial \phi}{\partial r} + \frac{1}{r^2}\frac{\partial^2 \phi}{\partial \theta^2} + \frac{\partial^2 \phi}{\partial z^2}. \qquad \bullet \qquad \bullet \qquad \bullet \qquad (24)$$

The components of $\nabla \times \mathbf{a}$ are

$$\frac{1}{r}\left\{\frac{\partial}{\partial \theta}(a_z) - \frac{\partial}{\partial z}(a_\theta r)\right\}, \quad \left\{\frac{\partial}{\partial z}(a_r) - \frac{\partial}{\partial r}(a_z)\right\}, \quad \frac{1}{r}\left\{\frac{\partial}{\partial r}(a_\theta r) - \frac{\partial}{\partial \theta}(a_r)\right\}.$$

$$(25)$$

§ **55.** Consider now any smooth closed curve L spanned by a smooth simple surface S. We can divide S into a number of very small areas $\Delta S_1, \Delta S_2, \ldots$ with perimeters $L_1, L_2 \ldots$ The sum of the line integrals round $L_1, L_2, \ldots$, all in the same sense, of a field vector $\mathbf{a}$ is the line integral round L: for all the other parts of the integrals cancel one another. Now for the curve L_k,

$$\mathrm{curl}_n \mathbf{a} = \frac{\displaystyle\int_{L_k} \mathbf{a} \cdot d\mathbf{l}}{\Delta S_k} + \epsilon_k,$$

where ϵ_k tends to zero with ΔS_k, and where $\mathrm{curl}_n \mathbf{a}$ is the normal component of curl $\mathbf{a}$ at some point in the area ΔS_k. Hence

$$\int_{L_k} \mathbf{a} \cdot d\mathbf{l} = (\mathrm{curl}_n \mathbf{a})\Delta S_k - \epsilon_k \Delta S_k$$

$$= (\mathrm{curl}\ \mathbf{a}) \cdot \Delta \mathbf{S}_k - \epsilon_k \Delta S_k,$$

so

$$\int_L \mathbf{a} \cdot d\mathbf{l} = \Sigma\ (\mathrm{curl}\ \mathbf{a}) \cdot \Delta \mathbf{S}_k - \Sigma \epsilon_k \Delta S_k.$$

Proceeding to the limiting case where $L_1, L_2, \ldots$ are infinitely small, we obtain

$$\int_L \mathbf{a} \cdot d\mathbf{l} = \int_S (\mathrm{curl}\ \mathbf{a}) \cdot d\mathbf{s} = \int_S (\nabla \times \mathbf{a}) \cdot d\mathbf{s}. \qquad . \qquad (26)$$

This is **Stokes's theorem**, which in non-vector notation reads

$$\int_L a_x dx + a_y dy + a_z dz$$
$$= \int_S \left[\left(\frac{\partial a_z}{\partial y} - \frac{\partial a_y}{\partial z} \right) \lambda + \left(\frac{\partial a_x}{\partial z} - \frac{\partial a_z}{\partial x} \right) \mu + \left(\frac{\partial a_y}{\partial x} - \frac{\partial a_x}{\partial y} \right) \nu \right] ds,$$

where λ, μ, ν are the direction cosines of the normal to ds.

In the same manner, if S be any smooth closed surface containing a volume V, we can divide V into a number of small volumes $\Delta V_1, \Delta V_2, \ldots$ with surfaces $S_1, S_2, \ldots$ The sum of the surface integrals over $S_1, S_2, \ldots$ of a field vector **a** is the surface integral over S. Also for any point inside S_k

$$\text{div } \mathbf{a} = \frac{\int_{S_k} \mathbf{a} \cdot d\mathbf{s}}{\Delta V_k} + \epsilon_k$$

where ϵ_k is an infinitesimal. Hence

$$\int_{S_k} \mathbf{a} \cdot d\mathbf{s} = (\text{div } \mathbf{a}) \Delta V_k - \epsilon_k \Delta V_k$$

so

$$\int_S \mathbf{a} \cdot d\mathbf{s} = \Sigma (\text{div } \mathbf{a}) \Delta V_k - \Sigma \epsilon_k \Delta V_k.$$

Proceeding to the limiting case where $S_1, S_2, \ldots$ are infinitely small we obtain

$$\int_S \mathbf{a} \cdot d\mathbf{s} = \int_V (\text{div } \mathbf{a}) dv = \int_V (\nabla \cdot \mathbf{a}) dv. \qquad \bullet \quad (27)$$

This is **Gauss's theorem**,* which in non-vector notation reads

$$\int_S (\lambda a_x + \mu a_y + \nu a_z) ds = \int_V \left(\frac{\partial a_x}{\partial x} + \frac{\partial a_y}{\partial y} + \frac{\partial a_z}{\partial z} \right) dv,$$

where λ, μ, ν are the direction cosines of the normal to ds.

* In many English textbooks this is known as *Green's* theorem.

The evaluation of $\int_V (\nabla \cdot \mathbf{a}) dv$ will involve triple integration and some textbooks show this by writing the integral $\iiint_V (\nabla \cdot \mathbf{a}) dv$. We have reserved the symbol dv to represent the element of volume so that no confusion will arise if we use only one integral sign.

Our proofs of Stokes's theorem and Gauss's theorem follow from our definitions of curl $\mathbf{a}$ and div $\mathbf{a}$. Some writers define curl $\mathbf{a} \equiv \nabla \times \mathbf{a}$ and div $\mathbf{a} \equiv \nabla \cdot \mathbf{a}$, in which case the above theorems would require different proofs.*

§ 56. Let ϕ_1 and ϕ_2 be any two functions which in the region considered are finite, one-valued and continuous and such that their first derivatives are continuous. Then by Gauss's theorem

$$\int_S (\phi_1 \nabla \phi_2) \cdot d\mathbf{s} = \int_V \nabla \cdot (\phi_1 \nabla \phi_2) dv$$

$$= \int_V \phi_1 \nabla^2 \phi_2 dv + \int_V (\nabla \phi_1) \cdot (\nabla \phi_2) dv. \quad (28)$$

Similarly

$$\int_S (\phi_2 \nabla \phi_1) \cdot d\mathbf{s} = \int_V \phi_2 \nabla^2 \phi_1 dv + \int_V (\nabla \phi_2) \cdot (\nabla \phi_1) dv.$$

Subtracting, we obtain

$$\int_V (\phi_1 \nabla^2 \phi_2 - \phi_2 \nabla^2 \phi_1) dv = \int_S (\phi_1 \nabla \phi_2 - \phi_2 \nabla \phi_1) \cdot d\mathbf{s}.$$

But $\nabla \phi_2 \cdot d\mathbf{s} = \dfrac{\partial \phi_2}{\partial n} ds$, where dn is the line element in the direction of the outward normal to ds. Hence

$$\int_V (\phi_1 \nabla^2 \phi_2 - \phi_2 \nabla^2 \phi_1) dv = \int_S \left(\phi_1 \frac{\partial \phi_2}{\partial n} - \phi_2 \frac{\partial \phi_1}{\partial n} \right) ds. \quad (29)$$

Both (28) and (29) are known as **Green's theorem**.

* Cf. Gillespie, *Integration* (2nd edition), pp. 56, 64.

A number of special cases are of importance.

(i) If $\phi_1 = \phi_2 = \phi$, then (28) gives

$$\int_S (\phi \nabla \phi) \cdot d\mathbf{s} = \int_V \phi \nabla^2 \phi \, dv + \int_V (\nabla \phi)^2 dv. \qquad . \qquad (30)$$

(ii) If $\phi_1 = $ constant, $\phi_2 = \phi$, then (29) reduces to

$$\int_V \nabla^2 \phi \, dv = \int_S \frac{\partial \phi}{\partial n} ds,$$

which is simply Gauss's theorem in the case where $\mathbf{a} = \nabla \phi$. If further $\nabla^2 \phi = 0$, we have

$$\int_S \frac{\partial \phi}{\partial n} ds = 0. \qquad . \qquad . \qquad . \qquad . \qquad (31)$$

(iii) If $\nabla^2 \phi_1 = \nabla^2 \phi_2 = 0$, then (29) yields

$$\int_S \phi_1 \frac{\partial \phi_2}{\partial n} ds = \int_S \phi_2 \frac{\partial \phi_1}{\partial n} ds, \qquad . \qquad . \qquad (32)$$

which is known as **Green's reciprocal theorem**.

(iv) As a particular case of (32) take $\phi_1 = 1/r$, $\phi_2 = \phi$, where r is the distance of ds from a fixed point P. It may be shown that $\nabla^2(1/r) = 0$ except at P. Thus (32) will be true for any surface S not enclosing P provided $\nabla^2 \phi$ is zero everywhere within S. We may take S as a surface enclosing P if we exclude the point P by an internal boundary formed of a small spherical surface Σ with P as centre. Then from (32) we obtain

$$\int_S \phi \frac{\partial}{\partial n}\left(\frac{1}{r}\right) ds + \int_\Sigma \phi \frac{\partial}{\partial n}\left(\frac{1}{r}\right) ds = \int_S \frac{1}{r} \frac{\partial \phi}{\partial n} ds + \int_\Sigma \frac{1}{r} \frac{\partial \phi}{\partial n} ds.$$

On the surface Σ, $\dfrac{\partial}{\partial n}\left(\dfrac{1}{r}\right) = -\dfrac{\partial}{\partial r}\left(\dfrac{1}{r}\right) = \dfrac{1}{r^2}$ and $ds = r^2 d\omega$, where $d\omega$ is the element of solid angle subtended by ds at P. Hence, neglecting infinitesimals,

$$\int_\Sigma \phi \frac{\partial}{\partial n}\left(\frac{1}{r}\right) ds = 4\pi \phi_{(P)},$$

and by (31)

$$\int_{\Sigma} \frac{1}{r} \frac{\partial \phi}{\partial n} ds = \frac{1}{r} \int_{\Sigma} \frac{\partial \phi}{\partial n} ds = 0.$$

Hence

$$\phi_{(P)} = \frac{-1}{4\pi} \int_S \phi \frac{\partial}{\partial n} \left(\frac{1}{r}\right) ds + \frac{1}{4\pi} \int_S \frac{1}{r} \frac{\partial \phi}{\partial n} ds. \quad . \quad (33)$$

This is an important result showing that *the value at a point* P, *of a function* ϕ *which satisfies* $\nabla^2 \phi = 0$ *everywhere within a closed surface* S *enclosing* P, *may be expressed in terms of the values of* ϕ *and* $\frac{\partial \phi}{\partial n}$ *on the surface* S.

§ 57.   **Examples**

(1) Show that $\nabla^2(r^n) = n(n+1)r^{n-2}$, where $r^2 = x^2 + y^2 + z^2$. Deduce that $\nabla^2(1/r) = 0$, except at $r = 0$.

(2) Show that if $\nabla^2 f(r) = 0$, then $f(r) = c_1/r + c_2$, where $r^2 = x^2 + y^2 + z^2$ and c_1 and c_2 are constants.

(3) Show that if $\nabla^2 f(R) = 0$, then $f(R) = c_1 \log R + c_2$, where $R^2 = x^2 + y^2$ and c_1 and c_2 are constants.

(4) Show that $r^a \mathbf{r}$ is an irrotational vector for any value of a, but is solenoidal only if $a = -3$.

(5) Show that if $(xyz)^b(x^a\mathbf{i} + y^a\mathbf{j} + z^a\mathbf{k})$ is irrotational, then either $b = 0$, or $a = -1$.

(6) Verify equations (8), (9), (10), (11), (12), (13) of § 52.

(7) Show that the volume enclosed by a closed surface S is $\frac{1}{6} \int_S \nabla(r^2) \cdot d\mathbf{s}$.

(8) Prove that $\nabla \cdot (\nabla \phi_1 \times \nabla \phi_2) \equiv 0$, where ϕ_1, ϕ_2 are arbitrary functions of x, y, z.

(9) Verify Stokes's theorem by evaluating $\int_L \mathbf{a} \cdot d\mathbf{l}$ and $\int_S (\nabla \times \mathbf{a}) \cdot d\mathbf{s}$ in the case where S is the hemisphere $r = c$ which has z everywhere positive, and where $\mathbf{a} = \mathbf{r} \times \mathbf{k}$.

(10) Show that $\int_S \mathbf{a} \cdot d\mathbf{s} = \frac{12}{5}\pi R^5$ where S is a sphere of radius R and $\mathbf{a} = x^3\mathbf{i} + y^3\mathbf{j} + z^3\mathbf{k}$.

(11) Use Gauss's theorem to prove the results

$$\int_V \nabla \phi \, dv = \int_S \phi \, d\mathbf{s}, \quad \int_V (\nabla \times \mathbf{c}) dv = -\int_S \mathbf{c} \times d\mathbf{s}.$$

CHAPTER V

POTENTIAL THEORY

§ 58. WE now ask an important question. Under what conditions can we represent a given field vector **a** as the gradient of a scalar function ϕ ?

If $\mathbf{a} = \nabla\phi$, then by § 52 (5), $\nabla \times \mathbf{a} = \mathbf{0}$, so that a necessary condition is curl $\mathbf{a} = \mathbf{0}$. We shall show that this is also a sufficient condition. If $\nabla \times \mathbf{a} = \mathbf{0}$, then by Stokes's theorem the line integral of **a** taken round any reducible closed curve is zero. Take the closed curve to be $OAPBO$ where O is an arbitrary fixed point and P is the point (x, y, z). Then

$$\int_{OAP} \mathbf{a} \cdot d\mathbf{l} + \int_{PBO} \mathbf{a} \cdot d\mathbf{l} = 0,$$

hence

$$\int_{OAP} \mathbf{a} \cdot d\mathbf{l} = \int_{OBP} \mathbf{a} \cdot d\mathbf{l}.$$

In other words $\int_{OP} \mathbf{a} \cdot d\mathbf{l}$ has the same value no matter what path is chosen for integration between O and P. Call the value of this integral ϕ. Evidently ϕ is a function of the coordinates (x, y, z) of P. ϕ will also involve the coordinates of O but these are constants. Take a point P' neighbouring to P and let $\int_{OP'} \mathbf{a} \cdot d\mathbf{l}$ be $\phi + \delta\phi$. Then

$$\phi + \delta\phi = \int_{OPP'} \mathbf{a} \cdot d\mathbf{l} = \int_{OP} \mathbf{a} \cdot d\mathbf{l} + \int_{PP'} \mathbf{a} \cdot d\mathbf{l} = \phi + \int_{PP'} \mathbf{a} \cdot d\mathbf{l} \, ;$$

hence,

$$\delta\phi = \int_{PP'} \mathbf{a} \cdot d\mathbf{l} = \mathbf{a} \cdot \delta\mathbf{l} = a_x \delta x + a_y \delta y + a_z \delta z.$$

78

It follows that

$$\frac{\partial \phi}{\partial x} = a_x, \quad \frac{\partial \phi}{\partial y} = a_y, \quad \frac{\partial \phi}{\partial z} = a_z.$$

In other words $\mathbf{a} = \nabla \phi$.

We have now shown that $\nabla \times \mathbf{a} = \mathbf{0}$ is the necessary and sufficient condition that a function ϕ exists whose gradient is $\mathbf{a}$. If we had taken a point O_1 instead of O we should have obtained a different function ϕ_1, which differed from ϕ by an additive constant only, for $\phi_1 - \phi = \int_{O_1 O} \mathbf{a} \cdot d\mathbf{l}$ and the right-hand side is a constant.

More generally, if ϕ and ϕ_1 be two solutions of $\nabla \phi = \mathbf{a}$ when $\nabla \times \mathbf{a} = \mathbf{0}$, then $\nabla(\phi - \phi_1) = \mathbf{a} - \mathbf{a} = \mathbf{0}$ and so

$$\frac{\partial}{\partial x}(\phi - \phi_1) = \frac{\partial}{\partial y}(\phi - \phi_1) = \frac{\partial}{\partial z}(\phi - \phi_1) = 0.$$

In other words $\phi - \phi_1$ must be a constant, since it does not involve x, y or z. Hence, two solutions of $\nabla \phi = \mathbf{a}$ differ by a constant only.

If $\mathbf{a}$ is irrotational we can find a function ϕ such that $\mathbf{a} = \nabla \phi$. It is equally easy to find a function ϕ such that $\mathbf{a} = -\nabla \phi$.

If $\mathbf{a}$ is irrotational and represents the gravitational field vector, then we write $\mathbf{a} = +\nabla \phi$ and call the function ϕ the **gravitational potential**.

If $\mathbf{a}$ is irrotational and represents the electric field vector, or, as it is more often called, the electric intensity, then we write $\mathbf{a} = -\nabla \phi$ and call the function ϕ the **electrostatic potential**.

If $\mathbf{a}$ is irrotational and represents the magnetic field vector, then we write $\mathbf{a} = -\nabla \phi$ and call the function ϕ the **magnetic potential**.

If $\mathbf{a}$ is irrotational and represents the velocity vector of a fluid, then we write $\mathbf{a} = -\nabla \phi$ and call the function ϕ the **velocity potential**.*

* Some authors write $\mathbf{a} = +\nabla \phi$ and call the function ϕ so obtained, the velocity potential.

§ **59.** A **field line** of a field vector **a** is a line such that at every point on it the direction of the line coincides with that of **a**. In diagrams we attach arrowheads to the field lines to indicate the direction. One field line will pass through every point of the field. Two field lines cannot intersect except at points where the field vector vanishes, for this would imply that the field vector had two directions

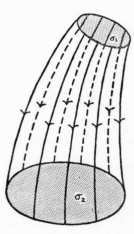

at the point of intersection. The differential equations of the field lines of a vector **a** are

$$\frac{dx}{a_x} = \frac{dy}{a_y} = \frac{dz}{a_z}. \qquad \bullet \qquad \bullet \qquad (1)$$

The reader is probably familiar with diagrams of lines of magnetic force. In this case certain field lines of the magnetic field vector are actually exhibited by scattering iron filings in the field. Again, if **a** be the velocity vector of a fluid, the field lines are the **stream lines** of the fluid.

The components of **a** may be functions of the time as well as of position, in which case the field lines vary with the time. A vector

FIG. 12

whose components do not involve the time is said to be **steady** or **stationary**.

The field lines through the points on a simple closed curve enclose a **field tube**. Each tube will have a direction associated with it, and, as in the case of the field lines, one can indicate the direction with arrowheads (fig. 12). Consider the volume bounded by the walls of a field tube and by two cross-sections σ_1 and σ_2. The surfaces σ_1 and σ_2 close a portion of the tube at its ends. If within this volume $\nabla \cdot \mathbf{a} = 0$, i.e., if the field is solenoidal within this volume, then by Gauss's theorem

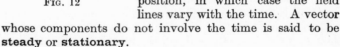

$$\int_S \mathbf{a} \cdot d\mathbf{s} = 0,$$

where S is composed of σ_1, σ_2 and the walls of the tube. Along the walls of the tube $\mathbf{a}$ is perpendicular to $d\mathbf{s}$ and so $\mathbf{a} \cdot d\mathbf{s} = 0$. Hence

$$\int_{\sigma_1} \mathbf{a} \cdot d\mathbf{s} + \int_{\sigma_2} \mathbf{a} \cdot d\mathbf{s} = 0,$$

where $d\mathbf{s}$ is drawn outwards in each case. It follows that

$$\int_\sigma \mathbf{a} \cdot d\mathbf{s} = \text{constant}$$

for all cross-sections σ, provided $d\mathbf{s}$ be drawn on the same side of σ in each case. With the stipulation that $d\mathbf{s}$ must always be drawn on the same side of σ as $\mathbf{a}$, we call the above constant the **strength** of the tube. A **unit tube** is one of unit strength, and a line drawn down the " middle " of a unit tube is sometimes called a **unit line**. The difficulty in using this latter terminology is that it is awkward to imagine a fraction of a unit line, while no such difficulty arises when we speak of a fraction of a unit tube.

We may imagine that all the space throughout which the field vector $\mathbf{a}$ is defined, can be filled with field tubes of $\mathbf{a}$ so that $\int_S \mathbf{a} \cdot d\mathbf{s}$ over a closed surface S gives the excess strength of the emergent tubes over the entrant tubes. For a closed surface S in the interior of which $\nabla \cdot \mathbf{a} = 0$ we have $\int_S \mathbf{a} \cdot d\mathbf{s} = 0$, which means that in a sole-noidal field the same number of tubes enter S as leave it. That is to say, field tubes or field lines cannot originate or terminate at a point where $\nabla \cdot \mathbf{a} = 0$.

§ 60. A point at which field tubes (or field lines) originate may be called a **source** and a point at which field tubes terminate may be called a **sink**. We have just seen that the divergence of the field vector cannot be zero at such points. A source at which tubes of total strength $4\pi m$ originate is called a source of **strength** m and a sink at which $4\pi m$ unit tubes terminate is a sink of strength m. We also regard a sink of strength m as being a source of strength $-m$.

If we suppose that the field is everywhere solenoidal except at a given source of strength m, then for any closed surface S surrounding this source

$$\int_S \mathbf{a} \cdot d\mathbf{s} = 4\pi m,$$

for $4\pi m$ represents the excess strength of the emergent tubes over the entrant tubes. More generally

$$\int_S \mathbf{a} \cdot d\mathbf{s} = 4\pi \text{ (total source strength within } S). \quad (2)$$

This equation is referred to as **Gauss's law**.

It might be well at this point to give a few examples of sources and sinks where the field vector has a physical significance.

If $\mathbf{a}$ be the velocity vector of a fluid, then $\mathbf{a} \cdot d\mathbf{s}$ will represent the volume of fluid flowing through the element ds per unit time, and $\int_S \mathbf{a} \cdot d\mathbf{s}$ represents the volume of fluid flowing out of the closed surface S per unit time. If the fluid be of constant density and the surface S contains only one source of strength m, then fluid is created at the source at the rate of $4\pi m$ units of volume per unit time. We know of course that fluid cannot be created at a point in the interior of a volume of fluid, but we have a close approximation to this when fluid emerges from a pipe whose outlet is in the interior of a fluid. A hydrodynamical source is a point where fluid is created and a sink is a point where fluid is annihilated.

The gravitational attractive field due to a material particle of mass m situated at the origin may be represented by the field vector $-(m/r^3)\mathbf{r}$, where the field is measured in attraction units and $\mathbf{r}$ is the position vector of the point at which the field is measured. This is merely a statement of **Newton's law of gravitation**. If we take $-(m/r^3)\mathbf{r}$ as the field vector $\mathbf{a}$ it may be easily shown that $\nabla \cdot \mathbf{a} = 0$ everywhere except at the origin. That is to say, field tubes can arise or terminate only at the origin where the particle of mass m is situated. If we evaluate $\int_S \mathbf{a} \cdot d\mathbf{s}$ where S is a sphere of radius R and centre the origin, we find that $\mathbf{a}$ has the same direction, apart from sign, as $d\mathbf{s}$ at every point of the sphere, that the magnitude of $\mathbf{a}$ at all points on the sphere is m/R^2 and that the magnitude of $d\mathbf{s}$ is $R^2 d\omega$, where $d\omega$ is the solid angle subtended by ds at the centre. Thus

$$\int_S \mathbf{a} \cdot d\mathbf{s} = -\int_S \frac{m}{R^2} R^2 d\omega = -4\pi m.$$

We see from this that a particle of mass m is equivalent to a sink of strength m, for at such a particle field tubes of total strength $4\pi m$ terminate.

The electric intensity in free space due to a point charge $+e$ at the origin is $+(e/r^3)\mathbf{r}$ by **Coulomb's law**. Hence in free space a particle of charge $+e$ is equivalent to a source of strength $+e$ of the field lines of electric intensity. This will not be true if space is filled with some medium. We shall discuss later in § **69** the modifications which are required when a medium is present.

We have not so far considered magnetic fields because, as we know, isolated magnetic poles do not exist. Equal and opposite poles always occur together. The N pole corresponds to a source and the S pole to a sink. The line drawn from the sink to the source of a rectilinear magnet is the **axis** of the magnet. If the strengths of the poles be m and $-m$ and the distance between the poles be l, then ml is called the **moment** of the magnet. A **magnetic particle** consists of an infinitely small magnet with a finite moment. The terms "**doublet**" and "**dipole**" are used instead of "magnetic particle" when dealing with similar configurations in vector fields other than magnetic ones.

If the closed surface S encloses a dipole, the dipole will contribute nothing to $\int_S \mathbf{a} \cdot d\mathbf{s}$ because the total algebraic source strength of a doublet is zero.

§ **61.** Unless we are dealing with the molecular structure of matter it is usual to treat matter as being continuous. From this point of view it is necessary to consider volume distributions of sources, sinks and dipoles. If we denote the volume density of source strength by ρ, where in general ρ is a function of position, we obtain

$$\int_S \mathbf{a} \cdot d\mathbf{s} = 4\pi \int_V \rho dv.$$

But

$$\int_S \mathbf{a} \cdot d\mathbf{s} = \int_V (\nabla \cdot \mathbf{a}) dv,$$

so

$$\int_V (\nabla \cdot \mathbf{a} - 4\pi \rho) dv = 0,$$

where V is any volume. If we take S and therefore V to be infinitely small, then we have, at any point in the field,

$$\nabla \cdot \mathbf{a} = 4\pi \rho. \quad . \quad . \quad . \quad . \quad (3)$$

If ρ represents the mass density of matter, then this formula takes the form

$$\nabla \cdot \mathbf{a} = -4\pi \rho, \quad . \quad . \quad . \quad . \quad (4)$$

since a material particle corresponds to a sink.

Suppose now that $\mathbf{a}$ is irrotational, i.e., $\nabla \times \mathbf{a} = \mathbf{0}$, then if $\mathbf{a}$ is the gravitational force vector we have

$$\nabla \cdot \mathbf{a} = -4\pi \rho \quad \text{and} \quad \mathbf{a} = +\nabla \phi,$$

whence

$$\nabla^2 \phi = -4\pi \rho.$$

If **a** be the velocity vector of a fluid or the electric intensity in free space, then

$$\nabla \cdot \mathbf{a} = +4\pi\rho \quad \text{and} \quad \mathbf{a} = -\nabla\phi,$$

whence
$$\nabla^2\phi = -4\pi\rho.$$

In each case

$$\nabla^2\phi \equiv \frac{\partial^2\phi}{\partial x^2} + \frac{\partial^2\phi}{\partial y^2} + \frac{\partial^2\phi}{\partial z^2} = -4\pi\rho, \quad . \quad . \quad (5)$$

which is **Poisson's equation.** In the absence of any source distribution, ϕ will satisfy **Laplace's equation**

$$\nabla^2\phi \equiv \frac{\partial^2\phi}{\partial x^2} + \frac{\partial^2\phi}{\partial y^2} + \frac{\partial^2\phi}{\partial z^2} = 0. \quad . \quad . \quad . \quad (6)$$

Laplace's equation is probably the most important equation in all physics.

§ **62.** We know that the charge on an electric conductor resides on the surface of the conductor (§ 68) ; it is there-fore necessary to consider surface distributions of sources. Let the surface density of the source strength, i.e., the source strength per unit area, be σ. In general σ is not a constant over the surface of distribution. Let us draw per-pendiculars to the surface at every point on the boundary of a small element of area ds, these perpendiculars extending a small distance on each side of the surface. We can close the cylindrical surface so formed by two small plane areas each equal and parallel to ds (fig. 13). Applying Gauss's law to this cylinder, we have

$$\int_S \mathbf{a} \cdot d\mathbf{s} = 4\pi \int_\Sigma \sigma ds,$$

where Σ is the area of the surface distribution enclosed by S. If we take the height of the cylinder to be infinitesimally small compared with the area of cross section, the above equation takes the form

$$\mathbf{a}_1 \cdot d\mathbf{s}_1 + \mathbf{a}_2 \cdot d\mathbf{s}_2 = 4\pi\sigma ds,$$

where $d\mathbf{s}_1$ and $d\mathbf{s}_2$ are normals to the surface of distribution and are drawn away from the sides 1 and 2 respectively, and where $\mathbf{a}_1$ and $\mathbf{a}_2$ represent the field vector very near to the element ds of the surface distribution on sides 1 and 2. We observe that $d\mathbf{s}_2 = -d\mathbf{s}_1$, and that the sense of $d\mathbf{s}_1$ is from side 2 to side 1. The last equation yields

$$(a_n)_1 - (a_n)_2 = 4\pi\sigma, \qquad . \qquad . \qquad . \qquad (7)$$

where $(a_n)_1$ and $(a_n)_2$ are the components of $\mathbf{a}$ in the direction of $d\mathbf{s}_1$ on sides 1 and 2 respectively. In other words,

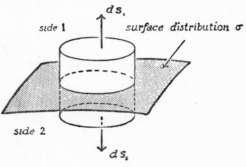

Fig. 13

as we pass from side 2 to side 1, the component of $\mathbf{a}$ normal to the surface in the direction $\overline{21}$ increases suddenly by an amount $4\pi\sigma$.

To avoid misunderstanding we shall recall that if $\mathbf{a}$ is the electric intensity, then only if no medium is present, are charges equivalent to sources; so the formula

$$\int_S \mathbf{a} \cdot d\mathbf{s} = 4\pi \text{ (total electric charge within S),}$$

where $\mathbf{a}$ is the electric intensity, will hold only in free space. It follows that equation (7) will hold only under these circumstances. We again refer the reader to § 69 for a treatment of the case when a medium is present.

If ϕ_1 and ϕ_2 be the potential functions of **a** on sides 1 and 2 of the surface distribution, then in the case $\mathbf{a} = -\nabla\phi$, we have

$$+\frac{\partial\phi_1}{\partial n} - \frac{\partial\phi_2}{\partial n} = -4\pi\sigma, \quad \bullet \quad \bullet \quad \bullet \quad (8)$$

where dn is drawn from the side 2 into the side 1. We obtain the same equation in the gravitational case, because although $\mathbf{a} = +\nabla\phi$, the surface density σ represents a distribution of sinks.

It may be shown that if only surface and volume distributions of sources are present, then the potential ϕ is continuous but the proof of this is beyond the scope of this book.* One might expect this result, however, from the fact that a discontinuity of potential would imply an infinite force or an infinite fluid velocity, according to the meaning of ϕ.

Let P and Q be two points close together on a surface of distribution or on a surface of separation between two media. Since ϕ is continuous, we have

$$\phi_{1(P)} = \phi_{2(P)}, \quad \phi_{1(Q)} = \phi_{2(Q)}.$$

It follows that

$$\frac{\phi_{1(Q)} - \phi_{1(P)}}{PQ} = \frac{\phi_{2(Q)} - \phi_{2(P)}}{PQ}$$

or

$$\frac{\partial\phi_1}{\partial t} = \frac{\partial\phi_2}{\partial t}, \quad \bullet \quad \bullet \quad \bullet \quad (9)$$

where dt is a line element lying in ds. In other words the components of **a** tangential to the surface, at points very near the surface, are the same on either side of it.

§ **63.** We have already seen that the field vector due to a source m at the origin is $(m/r^3)\mathbf{r}$. It is easily verified that this vector is irrotational so that a scalar potential

* See Kellogg, *Foundations of Potential Theory*, pp. 151, 160.

will exist and we now proceed to calculate this. We have, in fact, in the electrical and hydrodynamical cases,

$$-\nabla\phi = \frac{m}{r^3}\mathbf{r}.$$

Using spherical polar coordinates we obtain

$$-\frac{d\phi}{dr} = \frac{m}{r^2},$$

since ϕ cannot involve θ or ψ on account of spherical symmetry. Hence

$$\phi = \frac{m}{r}, \quad . \quad . \quad . \quad . \quad . \quad (10)$$

if we take the constant of integration to be zero, in which case ϕ vanishes at an infinite distance from the source. Thus in the theory of electricity a charge $+m$ gives rise to a potential $+m/r$ and in the theory of hydrodynamics a source of strength $+m$ gives rise to a potential $+m/r$.

In gravitational theory we find that

$$\nabla\phi = -\frac{m}{r^3}\mathbf{r},$$

which is the same equation as before. In other words, the potential due to a particle of mass m is $+m/r$. We observe that although a material particle corresponds to a sink, yet the potential is $+m/r$, not $-m/r$, the reason being that the field vector is $\nabla\phi$, not $-\nabla\phi$.

The potential due to a volume distribution of density ρ is evidently

$$\int \frac{\rho dv}{r}, \quad . \quad . \quad . \quad . \quad . \quad (11)$$

where ρ represents the hydrodynamical source density, the density of electric charge or the mass density, and where r is the distance of the element dv from the point at which the potential is being evaluated. The integral is taken over all the space occupied by the distribution.

Similarly the potential due to a surface distribution σ is

$$\int \frac{\sigma ds}{r}. \qquad . \qquad . \qquad . \qquad . \qquad . \qquad (12)$$

We are now able to construct a vector $\mathbf{b}'$ required in § 67, which has the properties $\nabla . \mathbf{b}' = -4\pi t$, $\nabla \times \mathbf{b}' = \mathbf{0}$. Comparing the first of these equations with (3), we see that $\mathbf{b}'$ is the field vector due to a volume distribution of sources of density $-t$, so that the potential of $\mathbf{b}'$ is

$$\phi = -\int \frac{tdv}{r}.$$

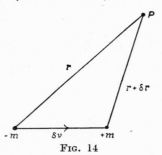

Fig. 14

Having evaluated this integral we obtain $\mathbf{b}' = -\nabla\phi$, which satisfies identically the condition $\nabla \times \mathbf{b}' = \mathbf{0}$. The required vector is therefore

$$\mathbf{b}' = \nabla\left(\int \frac{tdv}{r}\right).$$

§ 64. A dipole may be represented by a vector whose length is the moment of the dipole, and whose direction is that of the axis. We shall consider the potential at the point P, with coordinates (x, y, z), due to a dipole $\mathbf{w}$ at (x', y', z'). The dipole may be regarded as the limiting case of sources m and $-m$, distant $\delta\nu$ apart, where $\delta\nu$ is measured from the sink to the source (fig. 14). The potential at P is

$$\phi = -\frac{m}{r} + \frac{m}{r+\delta r} = m\delta\nu\left\{\left(\frac{1}{r+\delta r} - \frac{1}{r}\right)\Big/\delta\nu\right\}.$$

In the limiting case when $\delta\nu$ becomes infinitesimally small, the potential becomes

$$w\frac{\partial}{\partial\nu}\left(\frac{1}{r}\right) = w\left[\frac{\partial x'}{\partial\nu}\frac{\partial}{\partial x'}\left(\frac{1}{r}\right) + \frac{\partial y'}{\partial\nu}\frac{\partial}{\partial y'}\left(\frac{1}{r}\right) + \frac{\partial z'}{\partial\nu}\frac{\partial}{\partial z'}\left(\frac{1}{r}\right)\right],$$

since ν involves x', y', z' but not x, y, z. Now the direction cosines of $\mathbf{w}$ are $\dfrac{\partial x'}{\partial \nu}$, $\dfrac{\partial y'}{\partial \nu}$, $\dfrac{\partial z'}{\partial \nu}$ and

$$\frac{\partial}{\partial x'}\left(\frac{1}{r}\right) = -\frac{1}{r^2}\frac{\partial}{\partial x'}\left[(x'-x)^2 + (y'-y)^2 + (z'-z)^2\right]^{\frac{1}{2}}$$

$$= -\frac{2}{r^2}\cdot\frac{(x'-x)}{2r} = \frac{x-x'}{r^3}.$$

Similarly $\dfrac{\partial}{\partial y'}\left(\dfrac{1}{r}\right) = \dfrac{y-y'}{r^3}$ and $\dfrac{\partial}{\partial z'}\left(\dfrac{1}{r}\right) = \dfrac{z-z'}{r^3}$. The potential at (x, y, z) due to the dipole $\mathbf{w}$ at (x', y', z') is thus seen to be

$$\frac{w_x(x-x') + w_y(y-y') + w_z(z-z')}{r^3},$$

or

$$\frac{\mathbf{w}\cdot\mathbf{r}}{r^3},$$

where $\mathbf{r}$ is the vector drawn from the dipole to the point P. Sometimes it is more convenient to choose $\mathbf{r}$ as the vector from P to the dipole, in which case the potential at P is

$$-\frac{\mathbf{w}\cdot\mathbf{r}}{r^3}. \qquad \cdot \qquad \cdot \qquad \cdot \qquad \cdot \quad (13)$$

Thus if $\mathbf{p}$ be the resultant dipole moment density of a volume distribution of dipoles then the potential at P due to this distribution is

$$-\int\frac{\mathbf{p}\cdot\mathbf{r}}{r^3}dv, \qquad \cdot \qquad \cdot \qquad \cdot \quad (14)$$

the integral being taken over all the space which is occupied by the distribution and $\mathbf{r}$ being the vector drawn from P to the dipole element $\mathbf{p}dv$.

Now

$$\int_S \frac{\mathbf{p}\cdot d\mathbf{s}}{r} = \int_V \nabla\cdot\left(\frac{1}{r}\mathbf{p}\right)dv$$

$$= \int_V \frac{\nabla\cdot\mathbf{p}}{r}dv - \int_V \frac{\mathbf{p}\cdot\mathbf{r}}{r^3}dv.$$

So the potential at P due to the dipole distribution is

$$\int_S \frac{\mathbf{p} \cdot d\mathbf{s}}{r} - \int_V \frac{\nabla \cdot \mathbf{p}}{r} dv, \qquad . \qquad . \qquad . \quad (15)$$

where S is any surface enclosing all the distributions. When $\mathbf{p}$ is discontinuous on surfaces S', the first integral in (15) is replaced by a sum of surface integrals taken over S and S', where each S' is taken twice over, once with the normal in each direction. This amounts to adding a term

$$\int_{S'} \frac{\mathbf{p}' \cdot d\mathbf{s}}{r}$$

to the formula (15), where $\mathbf{p}' = \mathbf{p}_{\text{inside } S'} - \mathbf{p}_{\text{outside } S'}$. If we can choose S so large that $\mathbf{p}$ vanishes on S, the surface integral over S is zero and the potential at P becomes

$$\int_{S'} \frac{\mathbf{p}' \cdot d\mathbf{s}}{r} - \int \frac{\nabla \cdot \mathbf{p}}{r} dv, \qquad . \qquad . \qquad . \quad (16)$$

the volume integral being taken over all space. Comparing this result with (11) and (12) we see that if there is no dipole distribution at infinity a dipole distribution $\mathbf{p}$ may be replaced by a volume source distribution $-\nabla \cdot \mathbf{p}$ and a surface source distribution p'_n (the component of $\mathbf{p}'$ in the direction of $d\mathbf{s}$), without altering the potential or the field vector at any point. This has an important application in the theory of dielectrics (§ 69).

A surface distribution of dipoles whose direction is everywhere normal to the surface is often referred to as a **magnetic shell** on account of its application to electromagnetic theory. If τ be the dipole strength per unit area, then a small area $d\mathbf{s}$ of the surface gives rise to a dipole $\tau d\mathbf{s}$. The potential ϕ at P due to this element is $-(\tau/r^3) d\mathbf{s} \cdot \mathbf{r}$, where $\mathbf{r}$ is drawn from P to the element ds. If θ is the angle between $\mathbf{r}$ and $d\mathbf{s}$, then

$$\phi = -\frac{\tau r ds \cos \theta}{r^3} = -\frac{\tau r r^2 d\omega}{r^3} = -\tau d\omega, \qquad . \quad (17)$$

where $d\omega$ is the solid angle subtended at P by ds. The potential at P due to the whole shell is therefore $-\int\tau d\omega$ or, if the shell be uniform, the potential is

$$-\tau\Omega, \quad . \quad . \quad . \quad . \quad (18)$$

where Ω is the total solid angle subtended at P by the shell. In these results we assume that P is on the negative or sink side of the distribution. Otherwise the negative sign is replaced by a positive one. In view of this fact it will be evident that the potential due to an element of a magnetic shell increases suddenly from $-2\pi\tau$ to $+2\pi\tau$ as we pass through the element from the sink side to source side. There is, however, no sudden change in the potential due to the rest of the shell. We conclude therefore that the potential due to a magnetic shell increases by $4\pi\tau$ as we pass from the sink side to the source side.

§ **65.** In hydrodynamics we require the potentials of two dimensional sources and doublets. A three dimensional source of strength m is one such that, for any small surface surrounding it, $\int a_n ds = 4\pi m$. In two dimensions a source of strength m is one such that, for any small curve surrounding it, $\int a_n dl = 2\pi m$, where a_n is the component of **a** normal to ds or dl as the case may be. Taking the small curve to be a circle of radius r and whose centre is the source, we have

$$-2\pi r \frac{\partial\phi}{\partial r} = 2\pi m,$$

whence

$$\phi = -m \log r, \quad . \quad . \quad . \quad (19)$$

by choosing the constant of integration to be zero.

Again for a two-dimensional dipole **w** the potential is

$$\phi = m \log r - m \log (r + \delta r)$$
$$= -m \log \left(1 + \frac{\delta r}{r}\right).$$

If we now proceed to the limit as $\delta v \to 0$, then

$$\phi = -\frac{m\delta r}{r} = -\frac{m(-\delta v \cos \theta)}{r} = \frac{w \cos \theta}{r}$$

$$= \frac{\mathbf{w} \cdot \mathbf{r}}{r^2}, \qquad \cdot \quad \cdot \quad \cdot \quad \cdot \quad \cdot \quad \cdot \quad (20)$$

where $\mathbf{r}$ is drawn from the dipole to the point at which the potential is to be evaluated.

§ 66. We are now in a position to calculate the potential due to point sources, volume and surface distributions of sources, point dipoles, volume distributions of dipoles and also surface distributions of dipoles in which the dipole density is everywhere normal to the surface. The potential due to two or more of these being present together is simply the sum of the separate potentials, for

$$\nabla(\phi_1 + \phi_2) = \nabla\phi_1 + \nabla\phi_2,$$

and we know that the field vectors $\nabla\phi_1$ and $\nabla\phi_2$ due to different distributions are added according to the vector law to give the field vector due to the combination of the distributions.

If we know ϕ at all points in space we can connect all those points which have the same value C for ϕ by an **equipotential surface** $\phi(x, y, z) = C$. For different values of C we get different equipotential surfaces, one of which passes through any given point in space. As we have already shown in § 47, the field vector $\nabla\phi$ (or $-\nabla\phi$) is everywhere normal to the equipotential surfaces.

We shall now illustrate by an example a method of drawing equipotential surfaces in certain cases. We shall consider a point source in the presence of a uniform field ; e.g., a unit electric point charge placed in an electric field which has the value 6k at each point. The potential ϕ_1 due to the point charge is $1/r$ and the equipotential surfaces $\phi_1 = 1, 2, 3, \ldots$ are the spheres $r = 1, \frac{1}{2}, \frac{1}{3}, \ldots$ The diagram (fig. 15) represents the plane $y = 0$ and these spheres

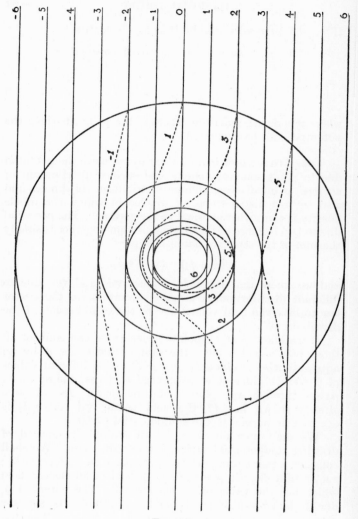

FIG. 15

are represented by circles in the diagram. For the sake of clarity we have only drawn the first six of these circles. We may take the potential ϕ_2 due to the uniform field to be $-6z$ for $-\nabla(-6z) = 6\mathbf{k}$, and the equipotential surfaces $\phi_2 = -6, -5, -4, -3, -2, -1, 0, 1, 2, 3, 4, 5, 6$ are the planes $z = 1, \frac{5}{6}, \frac{4}{6}, \frac{3}{6}, \frac{2}{6}, \frac{1}{6}, 0, -\frac{1}{6}, -\frac{2}{6}, -\frac{3}{6}, -\frac{4}{6}, -\frac{5}{6}, -1$ which are represented by straight lines in the diagram. If we connect up all the points for which $\phi_1 + \phi_2 = $ constant by a curve, this curve will represent the intersection of the plane $y = 0$ with an equipotential surface. In our diagram we have drawn with dotted lines the curves $\phi_1 + \phi_2 = -1, 1, 3, 5$. The equipotential surfaces will be obtained by rotating these curves about the Z axis. We observe that the curve $\phi_1 + \phi_2 = 5$ is in two parts, one of which is a closed curve surrounding the point charge at the origin.

§ **67.** We now consider a problem which bears a certain resemblance to that of § 58. What are the necessary and sufficient conditions that a vector $\mathbf{a}$ can be represented as the curl of another vector $\mathbf{b}$? If $\mathbf{a} = \nabla \times \mathbf{b}$, then $\nabla \cdot \mathbf{a} = 0$ by § 52 (6). Thus a necessary condition is that the divergence of $\mathbf{a}$ should vanish. Let us assume that

$$\frac{\partial a_x}{\partial x} + \frac{\partial a_y}{\partial y} + \frac{\partial a_z}{\partial z} = 0,$$

and consider the curl of the vector

$$\left(\int_{z_0}^{z} a_y dz - \theta(x, y) \right) \mathbf{i} + \left(- \int_{z_0}^{z} a_x dz \right) \mathbf{j} + 0\mathbf{k}.$$

The x and y components of the curl of this vector are respectively a_x and a_y. The z component is

$$-\int_{z_0}^{z} \left(\frac{\partial a_x}{\partial x} + \frac{\partial a_y}{\partial y} \right) dz + \frac{\partial \theta(x, y)}{\partial y} = \int_{z_0}^{z} \frac{\partial a_z}{\partial z} dz + \frac{\partial \theta(x, y)}{\partial y}$$

$$= a_z(x, y, z) - a_z(x, y, z_0) + \frac{\partial \theta(x, y)}{\partial y}$$

This will reduce to x_s if a function $\theta(x, y)$ can be found such that $\dfrac{\partial \theta}{\partial y} = a_s(x, y, z_0)$ for all values of x and y. The required function is evidently

$$\theta(x, y) = \int_{y_\bullet}^{y} a_z(x, y, z_0) dy.$$

we can therefore take

$$\mathbf{b} = \left(\int_{z_\bullet}^{z} a_y(x, y, z) dz - \int_{y_0}^{y} a_z(x, y, z_0) dy \right) \mathbf{i} + \left(-\int_{z_0}^{z} a_x(x, y, z) dz \right) \mathbf{j} + 0 \mathbf{k} \quad . \quad . \quad (21)$$

as a solution of $\mathbf{a} = \nabla \times \mathbf{b}$. In this formula y_0 and z_0 are the y and z coordinates of an arbitrary fixed point.

For such a solution the divergence of $\mathbf{b}$ will not in general vanish. Suppose that $t = \dfrac{1}{4\pi} \nabla \cdot \mathbf{b}$, so that t is a function of x, y, z. We have seen in § 63 how to construct a vector $\mathbf{b}'$ which satisfies the conditions $\nabla \times \mathbf{b}' = \mathbf{0}$ and $\nabla \cdot \mathbf{b}' = -4\pi t$. If we write $\mathbf{b}^\circ \equiv \mathbf{b} + \mathbf{b}'$, then

$$\nabla \times \mathbf{b}^\circ = \nabla \times \mathbf{b} + \nabla \times \mathbf{b}' = \mathbf{a} ;$$
$$\nabla \cdot \mathbf{b}^\circ = \nabla \cdot \mathbf{b} + \nabla \cdot \mathbf{b}' = 0.$$

Hence $\mathbf{b}^\circ$ is itself a solution of $\mathbf{a} = \nabla \times \mathbf{b}^\circ$ and it satisfies the additional condition $\nabla \cdot \mathbf{b}^\circ = 0$. The vector $\mathbf{b}^\circ$ thus obtained is called the **vector potential** * of $\mathbf{a}$. It is not unique but is indeterminate to the extent of a vector whose divergence and curl are both zero.

* In most textbooks on physics the vector potential is given as
$$\mathbf{b}^\circ = \frac{1}{4\pi} \int \frac{(\nabla \times \mathbf{a}) dv}{r}.$$

This result should only be used after verification that it does in fact supply a vector whose curl is the vector $\mathbf{a}$. In particular this formula cannot be used when $\mathbf{a}$ represents a uniform field, as the reader can easily verify.

§ **68.** Space does not permit of more than a very rough discussion of the nature of matter but we shall give a brief account of its electric properties. An atom of matter consists of a nucleus and a number of circumnuclear electrons. The electrons are the elements of negative electricity while the nucleus has a positive charge which exactly neutralises the total negative charge of the circumnuclear electrons. An atom in its normal state has therefore no charge. **Insulators** or **dielectrics** are substances whose atoms normally keep all their circumnuclear electrons when in an applied electric field, **conductors** those whose electrons drift away when the substance is in an electric field. The drifting of the electrons produces an **electric current.** Atoms which are stripped of their electrons will have a positive charge while those to which the electrons drift will acquire a negative charge. Thus when a conductor is placed in an electric field certain electrons will move against the field lines until an equilibrium position is reached, in which some parts of the conductor will have a positive charge and others a negative charge. The equilibrium position will be attained almost instantaneously. In an equilibrium position there can be no force at any point in the interior of the conductor for otherwise the circumnuclear electrons of the atoms at this point would begin to move away from their parent atoms and the position would not be one of equilibrium. Since there is no force at any point in a conductor the electrostatic potential of the conductor must be constant throughout, and the surface of the conductor be an equipotential surface, so that the field lines just outside the conductor are everywhere normal to the surface. Again, since ϕ is a constant throughout the conductor, $\nabla^2\phi = 0$ within the conductor, showing that there is no net charge on any of the atoms in the interior of the conductor. Charges have, however, been built up on the surface of the conductor and the field in the interior is due to these induced charges as well as to the external electric field, so charges accumulate on the surface, of an

H

amount which will produce a field in the interior which exactly cancels the external field.

§ 69. In an insulator the circumnuclear electrons cannot leave the atom; but they may rearrange themselves inside the atom when the atom is in an electric field. The result of this will be that the atom becomes **polarised**. It will have a negative charge at one end and a positive one at the other, and may be regarded as a dipole. The direction of the dipole will be exactly that of the field line passing through the atom and the strength may be expected to be proportional to the electric field.* Thus when an insulator is in an electric field we find, set up in it, a **polarisation** or dipole density p, where p is proportional to the electric intensity † which we shall now denote by **E**. We have seen in § 64 that **E** is unaltered at any point if we replace the polarisation p by a source distribution of density $- \nabla . \mathbf{p}$ within the insulator, and a surface source distribution of strength p'_n on the surface of the insulator. We suppose that there is already a source distribution present specified by ρ and σ. Hence as far as the intensity is concerned we have a source distribution, in free space, specified by $\rho - \nabla . \mathbf{p}$ and $\sigma + p'_n$. We may therefore apply Gauss's law and obtain

$$\int_S \mathbf{E} . d\mathbf{s} = 4\pi \int_V (\rho - \nabla . \mathbf{p}) dv + 4\pi \int_{S'} (\sigma + p'_n) ds,$$

where S' denotes surfaces within S on which there is a surface distribution $\sigma + p'_n$.

* In certain crystalline bodies this is not the case.
† We define the electric intensity within a polarised medium as the field strength measured within a limitingly small needle-shaped cavity cut from the medium, in the direction of the field line. The shape of the cavity is important: in a spherical cavity the field strength would be $\mathbf{E} + \frac{4}{3}\pi\mathbf{p}$, while in a " penny-shaped " cavity, cut normal to the field line, it would be $\mathbf{E} + 4\pi\mathbf{p}$. This ambiguity does not arise in the definition of **E** within a source distribution without dipoles. For a complete discussion of this point, see J. G. Leathem, *Volume and Surface Integrals used in Physics*, and G. H. Livens, *The Theory of Electricity*, Ch. V.

Hence

$$\int_S (\mathbf{E} + 4\pi\mathbf{p}) \cdot d\mathbf{s} = 4\pi \int_V \rho dv + 4\pi \int_{S'} \sigma ds.$$

If we now define the **electric displacement D** by

$$\mathbf{D} \equiv \mathbf{E} + 4\pi\mathbf{p}, \quad . \quad . \quad . \quad . \quad (22)$$

then

$$\int_S \mathbf{D} \cdot d\mathbf{s} = 4\pi \text{ (total electric charge within S)}.$$

This vector **D** satisfies Gauss's law whether or not a medium be present. If, as usually happens, **p** is proportional to **E** then **D** is proportional to **E** and we may write

$$\mathbf{D} = \kappa\mathbf{E},$$

where κ is the **dielectric constant**. κ is evidently unity when the medium is a vacuum. We observe that, if $\sigma = 0$,

$$4\pi \int_V \rho dv = \int_S \mathbf{D} \cdot d\mathbf{s} = \int_V (\nabla \cdot \mathbf{D})dv,$$

so $\nabla \cdot \mathbf{D} = 4\pi\rho$ in all circumstances, whence if κ is independent of position,

$$\nabla \cdot \mathbf{E} = 4\pi\rho/\kappa. \quad . \quad . \quad . \quad (23)$$

Also, since $\mathbf{E} = -\nabla\phi$ we find that when ϕ is the electrostatic potential, equation (5) takes the form

$$\nabla^2\phi = \frac{\partial^2\phi}{\partial x^2} + \frac{\partial^2\phi}{\partial y^2} + \frac{\partial^2\phi}{\partial z^2} = -4\pi\rho/\kappa. \quad . \quad . \quad (24)$$

These equations will reduce to $\nabla \cdot \mathbf{E} = 4\pi\rho$ and $\nabla^2\phi = -4\pi\rho$ in free space, since κ is then unity.

The vector **D** is independent of the presence of a dielectric medium, and is therefore equal to the value of **E**, when no dielectric is present. It follows that the displacement due to a point charge $+e$ at the origin is $(e/r^3)\mathbf{r}$, so that a particle of charge $+e$ is always equivalent to a source of strength e of the displacement vector. Further, since $\mathbf{D} = \kappa\mathbf{E}$ the intensity due to a point charge e at the origin is $(e/\kappa r^3)\mathbf{r}$. This is a modified form of Coulomb's law.

Formula (7) now takes the form

$$(D_n)_1 - (D_n)_2 = 4\pi\sigma,$$

or

$$\kappa_1(E_n)_1 - \kappa_2(E_n)_2 = 4\pi\sigma,$$

whence

$$\kappa_1\frac{\partial\phi_1}{\partial n} - \kappa_2\frac{\partial\phi_2}{\partial n} = -4\pi\sigma, \quad . \quad . \quad . \quad (25)$$

κ_1 and κ_2 being the dielectric constants on sides 1 and 2 of the surface distribution σ. Equation (25) replaces equation (8) in the electric case but equation (9) holds good under all circumstances.

At a surface of separation between two dielectric media on which no surface distribution is present we have

$$\left.\begin{array}{l} \kappa_1\dfrac{\partial\phi_1}{\partial n} = \kappa_2\dfrac{\partial\phi_2}{\partial n}, \\[2mm] \dfrac{\partial\phi_1}{\partial t} = \dfrac{\partial\phi_2}{\partial t}, \end{array}\right\} \quad . \quad . \quad . \quad (26)$$

showing that the field lines are refracted on passing from one medium to another.

§ 70.   Examples

(1) Show that the field lines of $\nabla(x^2 - y^2)$ are rectangular hyperbolae and that those of $\nabla\{\tan^{-1}(y/x)\}$ are circles.

(2) The velocity vector of a fluid is $(xyz)\mathbf{r}$. Show that the vortex lines lie on spheres and also on certain cubic surfaces.

(3) Show that the stream lines due to a two-dimensional dipole are circles.

(4) Find a vector potential for $(1/r^3)\mathbf{r}$.

$$\frac{yz}{3r}\left(\frac{1}{x^2+y^2} - \frac{1}{x^2+z^2}\right)\mathbf{i} + \frac{zx}{3r}\left(\frac{1}{y^2+z^2} - \frac{1}{y^2+x^2}\right)\mathbf{j} + \frac{xy}{3r}\left(\frac{1}{z^2+x^2} - \frac{1}{z^2+y^2}\right)\mathbf{k}$$

is a symmetrical solution.

(5) Show that, for the system consisting of two point

charges $+4e$ and $-e$, one of the equipotential surfaces is a sphere. Sketch the equipotential surfaces for this system.

(6) Sketch the equipotential surfaces of $\phi = r_1 + r_2$, where r_1, r_2 are the distances from two fixed points. Sketch the equipotential surfaces of $\phi = r_1 - r_2$ on the same diagram.

(7) Sketch the equipotential surfaces of $\phi = y + \tan^{-1}(y/x)$.

(8) Show that the potential of a uniform circular disc of radius a, at a point on its axis at distance x from the disc, is $2\pi\sigma(\sqrt{a^2 + x^2} - x)$.

(9) Deduce from the last problem that the potential of a uniform sphere of mass M and radius a is given by $\phi_{r>a} = M/r$, $\phi_{r<a} = M(3a^2 - r^2)/2a^3$.

(10) Deduce from the last problem that the potential of a uniform spherical shell of mass M and radius a is given by $\phi_{r>a} = M/r$, $\phi_{r<a} = M/a$.

(11) Show that the electric intensity due to a uniformly charged sphere at points outside is the same as if the charge were concentrated at the centre, while at points inside the sphere it is proportional to the distance from the centre.

(12) Show that the displacement just outside a conductor is $4\pi\sigma$, where σ is the density of the surface charge.

(13) Calculate the potential due to a uniformly polarised sphere. Show that the electric intensity at any point in the interior is $-\frac{4}{3}\pi\mathbf{p}$, where $\mathbf{p}$ is the polarisation.

(14) A rectangular block has uniform polarisation $\mathbf{p}$ parallel to one edge. Show that the intensity and potential are unaltered if we replace the polarisation by a surface distribution of density p on one face and a distribution of density $-p$ on the opposite face.

CHAPTER VI

HYDRODYNAMICS

§ **71.** In this chapter we shall denote the velocity vector of a fluid by **u**. We shall confine our attention to frictionless fluids. In such a fluid it may be shown that the pressure p is the same in every direction.* We shall denote the mass density of the fluid by ρ and the source (volume) density by τ. Thus, at an element of volume dv there are $4\pi\tau dv$ units of volume and $4\pi\tau\rho dv$ units of mass of fluid created per second. If **F**, the external force per unit mass, be conservative, we can write $\mathbf{F} = -\nabla K$, where K is the potential energy. If the motion of the fluid is irrotational, a velocity potential ϕ will exist, for which $\mathbf{u} = -\nabla\phi$. If the motion is rotational a velocity potential will not exist, but there will be a vorticity vector **w** defined by the equation

$$\mathbf{w} = \nabla \times \mathbf{u}.$$

It is evident that **w** is a solenoidal vector.

The differential equations of the stream lines are

$$\frac{dx}{u_x} = \frac{dy}{u_y} = \frac{dz}{u_z}, \qquad \cdot \qquad \cdot \qquad \cdot \qquad \cdot \qquad (1)$$

and those of the vortex lines are

$$\frac{dx}{\dfrac{\partial u_z}{\partial y} - \dfrac{\partial u_y}{\partial z}} = \frac{dy}{\dfrac{\partial u_x}{\partial z} - \dfrac{\partial u_z}{\partial x}} = \frac{dz}{\dfrac{\partial u_y}{\partial x} - \dfrac{\partial u_x}{\partial y}} \qquad \cdot \qquad \cdot \qquad (2)$$

It should be observed that, unless the motion is steady,

* See H. Lamb, *Hydrodynamics*, p. 2.

the paths of the particles of fluid are not necessarily the stream lines. The differential equations of the paths are

$$\frac{dx}{dt} = u_x, \quad \frac{dy}{dt} = u_y, \quad \frac{dz}{dt} = u_z. \qquad . \qquad . \qquad (3)$$

We see that there are a triply infinite set of paths, one in fact for each particle, but only a doubly infinite set of stream lines, one through each point of any given surface which stretches across the fluid.

§ 72. Consider now a particle of fluid which at time t is at (x, y, z) and at time $t + \delta t$ is at $(x + \delta x, y + \delta y, z + \delta z)$. If $H(x, y, z, t)$ be any property of the particle, as for example its density, then

$$\delta H = \frac{\partial H}{\partial x}\delta x + \frac{\partial H}{\partial y}\delta y + \frac{\partial H}{\partial z}\delta z + \frac{\partial H}{\partial t}\delta t.$$

The rate of increase of H with respect to the time is

$$\frac{dx}{dt}\frac{\partial H}{\partial x} + \frac{dy}{dt}\frac{\partial H}{\partial y} + \frac{dz}{dt}\frac{\partial H}{\partial z} + \frac{\partial H}{\partial t},$$

or

$$u_x\frac{\partial H}{\partial x} + u_y\frac{\partial H}{\partial y} + u_z\frac{\partial H}{\partial z} + \frac{\partial H}{\partial t}.$$

This last expression is usually denoted by $\frac{DH}{Dt}$ and it denotes differentiation following the motion of the fluid. Thus, $\frac{D\rho}{Dt}$ denotes the rate of change of the density ρ *of a particle* of the fluid, but $\frac{\partial \rho}{\partial t}$ denotes the rate of change of ρ *at a particular point in space.* Evidently

$$\frac{DH}{Dt} = \frac{\partial H}{\partial t} + \mathbf{u} \cdot \nabla H ; \qquad . \qquad . \qquad . \qquad (4)$$

in particular, by § 52 (13),

$$\frac{D\mathbf{u}}{Dt} = \frac{\partial \mathbf{u}}{\partial t} + (\mathbf{u} \cdot \nabla)\mathbf{u} = \frac{\partial \mathbf{u}}{\partial t} + \frac{1}{2}\nabla \mathbf{u}^2 + (\nabla \times \mathbf{u}) \times \mathbf{u}. \quad . \quad (5)$$

§ **73.** Consider a closed simple surface S drawn within a fluid. The mass of fluid flowing out of S per unit time is

$$\int_S \rho \mathbf{u} \cdot d\mathbf{s} \quad \text{or} \quad \int_V \nabla \cdot (\rho \mathbf{u}) dv.$$

This fluid may be accounted for in two ways. Firstly, a decrease in the density ρ of the fluid within S will cause a mass

$$-\int_V \frac{\partial \rho}{\partial t} dv$$

per unit time to flow outwards. Secondly, a source distribution τ will contribute a mass

$$4\pi \int_V \rho \tau dv.$$

Hence,

$$4\pi \int_V \rho \tau dv - \int_V \frac{\partial \rho}{\partial t} dv = \int_V \nabla \cdot (\rho \mathbf{u}) \, dv.$$

It follows that at any point in the fluid, we have

$$\frac{\partial \rho}{\partial t} + \nabla \cdot (\rho \mathbf{u}) = 4\pi \tau \rho,$$

which may be written

$$\frac{D\rho}{Dt} + \rho \nabla \cdot \mathbf{u} = 4\pi \tau \rho. \quad . \quad . \quad . \quad (6)$$

If the fluid is incompressible this last equation yields

$$\nabla \cdot \mathbf{u} = 4\pi \tau, \quad . \quad . \quad . \quad . \quad (7)$$

and if it is also irrotational we have Poisson's equation

$$\nabla^2 \phi = -4\pi \tau. \quad . \quad . \quad . \quad (8)$$

For an incompressible fluid in the absence of sources (7) takes the simple form

$$\nabla \cdot \mathbf{u} = 0. \quad . \quad . \quad . \quad . \quad (9)$$

Equation (6), of which (7), (8) and (9) are special cases, is known as the **equation of continuity**. It expresses the fact that holes do not occur in a fluid.

§ **74.** We shall now obtain the equations of motion of a frictionless fluid. We do this by considering the forces acting on an element of fluid whose volume is $\delta x \delta y \delta z$ and whose mass is $\rho \delta x \delta y \delta z$. There will be a force on one end in the direction $\overline{OX}$ of magnitude $p \delta y \delta z$ due to the pressure on this end, and on the opposite end a force of magnitude $\left(p + \dfrac{\partial p}{\partial x} \delta x \right) \delta y \delta z$ in the opposite direction. The resultant force in the $\overline{OX}$ direction due to the pressure will be $-\dfrac{\partial p}{\partial x} \delta x \delta y \delta z$. The external force in this direction will be $F_x \rho \delta x \delta y \delta z$. The acceleration of the element in the $\overline{OX}$ direction will be $\dfrac{Du_x}{Dt}$. Hence

$$F_x \rho \delta x \delta y \delta z - \frac{\partial p}{\partial x} \delta x \delta y \delta z = \frac{Du_x}{Dt} \rho \delta x \delta y \delta z.$$

In this manner we deduce **Euler's equations of motion**

$$\frac{Du_x}{Dt} = F_x - \frac{1}{\rho} \frac{\partial p}{\partial x}, \quad \frac{Du_y}{Dt} = F_y - \frac{1}{\rho} \frac{\partial p}{\partial y}, \quad \frac{Du_z}{Dt} = F_z - \frac{1}{\rho} \frac{\partial p}{\partial z},$$

which may be combined into the single vector equation

$$\frac{D\mathbf{u}}{Dt} = \mathbf{F} - \frac{1}{\rho} \nabla p. \qquad . \qquad . \qquad . \qquad (10)$$

If the external force is conservative, then with the help of (5) this may be written in the form

$$\frac{\partial \mathbf{u}}{\partial t} + \frac{1}{2} \nabla \mathbf{u}^2 + (\nabla \times \mathbf{u}) \times \mathbf{u} = -\nabla K - \frac{1}{\rho} \nabla p. \qquad . \qquad (11)$$

In the case of irrotational motion we have

$$\nabla \times \mathbf{u} = \mathbf{0}, \quad \mathbf{u} = -\nabla \phi, \quad \frac{\partial \mathbf{u}}{\partial t} = -\nabla \frac{\partial \phi}{\partial t}$$

and (11) takes the form

$$\nabla\left(-\frac{\partial\phi}{\partial t} + \tfrac{1}{2}u^2 + K \right) + \frac{1}{\rho}\nabla p = \mathbf{0}.$$

on forming the scalar product of both sides with $d\mathbf{1}$, we obtain

$$d\left(-\frac{\partial\phi}{\partial t} + \tfrac{1}{2}u^2 + K \right) + \frac{1}{\rho}dp = 0$$

from which we obtain **Bernoulli's equation**

$$-\frac{\partial\phi}{\partial t} + \tfrac{1}{2}u^2 + K + \int\frac{dp}{\rho} = \psi$$

where ψ is a function of the time, since we have integrated along an arbitrary path in the fluid at a given instant. In the case where ρ is constant and the motion is steady this equation takes the form

$$\tfrac{1}{2}u^2 + K + p/\rho = \psi, . \qquad . \qquad . \qquad . \quad (12)$$

where ψ is now a constant. This states that per unit mass the kinetic energy $\tfrac{1}{2}u^2$ plus the potential energy K plus what we may call the pressure energy p/ρ has a constant value ψ at all points of the fluid.

Equation (12) can also be obtained for the case of steady rotational motion provided that $(\nabla \times \mathbf{u}) \times \mathbf{u} = \mathbf{0}$. That is, provided $\mathbf{w}$ has the same direction as $\mathbf{u}$ at each point of the fluid. In such a case the vortex lines coincide with the stream lines.

In problems in aerodynamics the variations in K are usually so small that they can be neglected, so that we can write

$$\tfrac{1}{2}\rho u^2 + p = p_0, \qquad . \qquad . \qquad . \qquad . \quad (13)$$

where p_0 is the pressure when the fluid is at rest. We see that in such circumstances the pressure diminishes as the velocity increases. Aeroplanes are fitted with instruments for measuring p and p_0, so that the velocity of the machine relative to the air can be determined.

In the case of steady rotational motion of an incompressible fluid, (11) can be written

$$(\mathbf{u} \cdot \nabla)\mathbf{u} + \nabla K + \frac{1}{\rho}\nabla p = \mathbf{0}.$$

If we form the scalar product of the above equation with **u** we obtain

$$\mathbf{u} \cdot \nabla \frac{u^2}{2} + \mathbf{u} \cdot \nabla K + \frac{1}{\rho}\mathbf{u} \cdot \nabla p = 0.$$

But $\dfrac{DH}{Dt} = \mathbf{u} \cdot \nabla H$ if the motion is steady, so

$$\frac{D}{Dt}\left(\frac{u^2}{2} + K + \frac{p}{\rho}\right) = 0.$$

Hence, integrating along a stream line, we have

$$\frac{u^2}{2} + K + \frac{p}{\rho} = \psi . \qquad . \qquad . \qquad . \qquad (14)$$

where ψ is a constant for the stream line in question. It should be noted that (14) has a different meaning from (12). In (12) ψ is a constant throughout the fluid, but in (14) ψ may have different values for different stream lines although it is a constant for every point of a given stream line. As we have seen, ψ has the same value for each stream line if the motion is irrotational or if the vortex lines coincide with the stream lines.

§ **75.** We have seen in § 59 that since **w** is everywhere solenoidal, vortex tubes or lines cannot originate or terminate at any point in the interior of a fluid. It follows that a vortex line must either form a closed curve, as in the familiar example of a smoke ring, or else it must begin and end on the boundary of the fluid, as in the case of a whirlpool.

Again, $\displaystyle\int \mathbf{w} \cdot d\mathbf{s}$ has a constant value for any cross-section S of a given vortex tube and, since $\mathbf{w} = \nabla \times \mathbf{u}$, this integral can be expressed as $\displaystyle\int_L \mathbf{u} \cdot d\mathbf{l}$ by using Stokes's theorem, where L is any simple closed curve drawn on the walls of the tube and surrounding it. The integral

$$\int_L \mathbf{u} \cdot d\mathbf{l}$$

is called the **circulation** round the closed curve L and measures the total strength of all the vortex tubes passing through L, provided that the curve L can be contracted to a point, without any part of the curve passing out of the fluid. It is possible, however, for a circulation round L to exist even when the fluid is everywhere irrotational. This may happen, for example, in the case where there is an infinite solid cylinder passing through L. The solid cylinder can in fact behave like a vortex filament in an otherwise irrotational fluid. We shall treat this in some detail in the next paragraph.

§ **76.** The case of an infinite cylinder in a fluid whose motion is everywhere perpendicular to the axis of the cylinder, may be discussed by investigating the nature of the two dimensional potential

$$\phi = -\frac{\kappa\theta}{2\pi} = -\frac{\kappa}{2\pi}\tan^{-1}\frac{y}{x}. \quad \bullet \quad \bullet \quad (15)$$

We observe that this potential is not defined when $r = 0$, and that elsewhere ϕ is a many-valued function of the position in the plane OXY. The existence of such a potential means that the motion is irrotational except along the axis OZ where no potential is defined. Also, the stream lines are concentric circles since $-\dfrac{\partial\phi}{\partial r} = 0$, and the velocity of the fluid at any point is therefore $-\dfrac{1}{r}\dfrac{\partial\phi}{\partial\theta}$ or $\dfrac{\kappa}{2\pi r}$. The circulation $\displaystyle\int_L \mathbf{u} \cdot d\mathbf{l}$ round any circle of radius a whose centre is the origin is

$$\int_0^{2\pi} \frac{\kappa}{2\pi a} a\,d\theta = \kappa,$$

indicating that there is a vortex filament of strength κ lying along the axis OZ. It follows that the potential (15) represents a single vortex filament of strength κ in an otherwise irrotational fluid. We can now replace this filament by an infinite cylinder which encloses it. In this case the motion is everywhere irrotational, but the potential is only defined outside the cylinder and there is a circulation κ round the cylinder.

The potential due to an infinite circular cylinder of radius a whose axis at the instant under consideration is the line OZ, and which is moving without circulation in an infinite ocean and with velocity V in the direction $\overline{OX}$, may be shown to be *

$$\frac{Va^2 \cos \theta}{r}, \quad (r > a).$$

If we superimpose a circulation κ round the cylinder, the combined potential is

$$\phi = \frac{Va^2 \cos \theta}{r} - \frac{\kappa \theta}{2\pi}.$$

Whence,

$$-\frac{1}{r}\frac{\partial \phi}{\partial \theta} = \frac{Va^2 \sin \theta}{r^2} + \frac{\kappa}{2\pi r}, \quad -\frac{\partial \phi}{\partial r} = \frac{Va^2 \cos \theta}{r^2},$$

and

$$u^2 = \frac{V^2 a^4}{r^4} + \frac{2Va^2\kappa \sin \theta}{2\pi r^3} + \frac{\kappa^2}{4\pi^2 r^2}.$$

That is to say

$$u_{\theta = +\pi/2} = \frac{Va^2}{r^2} + \frac{\kappa}{2\pi r}, \quad u_{\theta = -\pi/2} = \frac{Va^2}{r^2} - \frac{\kappa}{2\pi r},$$

showing, as we would expect, that the velocity is greater where $\theta = +\frac{1}{2}\pi$ than where $\theta = -\frac{1}{2}\pi$. From Bernoulli's equation † we deduce that the pressure on the cylinder must be less where $\theta = +\frac{1}{2}\pi$ than it is where $\theta = -\frac{1}{2}\pi$.

This result has some important applications. A rotor ship has revolving funnel-like cylinders which induce a

* Cf. Ex. 6, p. 122.

† To evaluate the actual pressures we cannot use the simplified equation (12) as, with the above choice of axes, the motion is not steady.

circulation. The combination of this circulation with a transverse wind produces a state of affairs similar to the case described above. The pressure difference which arises is the force which propels the ship.

If we neglect the end-effects, the wing of an aeroplane may be regarded as a cylinder moving through the air in a direction perpendicular to its axis. The cross-section of the wing is so designed that the frictional forces set up a circulation, with the result that the pressure on the under side of the wing is greater than that on the upper side. It is this difference of pressure which balances gravity and keeps a heavier-than-air machine in the air.

§ 77.   Examples

(1) A source-free fluid of constant density is everywhere irrotational within the surface S. Use Green's theorem to show that the kinetic energy of the fluid within S is $\frac{1}{2}\rho\int_{S}\phi\frac{\partial\phi}{\partial n}ds$. Using Ex. (11) § 57, prove also that the momentum and the moment of momentum about the origin of the fluid within S are respectively $-\rho\int_{S}\phi d\mathbf{s}$ and $-\rho\int_{S}\phi\mathbf{r}\times d\mathbf{s}$.

(2) A sphere of radius a moving with velocity V in the direction OX ($x=r\cos\theta$) through a liquid which is at rest at infinity has a potential $\phi=\frac{1}{2}V(a^3/r^2)\cos\theta$ at the instant when the centre of the sphere is at the origin. Show that the kinetic energy of the liquid is $MV^2/4$, where M is the mass of the fluid displaced. Show also that the total momentum of the liquid is zero.

(3) Prove that the resultant moment of momentum about the centre of the fluid contained within a spherical surface vanishes if the fluid is irrotational, source-free and of constant density at each point within the surface.

(4) If the stream lines of a source-free fluid of constant density are the intersections of the surfaces $f_1 = $ constant, $f_2 = $ constant, prove that
$$\mathbf{u} = F(f_1, f_2)(\nabla f_1 \times \nabla f_2).$$

CHAPTER VII

LAPLACE'S EQUATION

§ 78. A FURTHER discussion of Laplace's equation is necessary. If ϕ be any continuous one-valued function which satisfies $\nabla^2\phi = 0$, and is not infinite in a given region, then ϕ cannot have a maximum or a minimum at any point within this region. For if it had, it would be possible to draw a small surface surrounding such a point for which $\int\nabla\phi \cdot d\mathbf{s} \neq 0$. This would imply $\int\nabla^2\phi \, dv \neq 0$, in contradiction to our supposition that $\nabla^2\phi = 0$ everywhere within the region.

It follows that if $\nabla^2\phi = 0$ everywhere within a closed boundary, and ϕ has a constant value on this boundary, then ϕ must take this value everywhere within the boundary. Otherwise it would have a maximum or a minimum at some point within the boundary.

As we have seen in § 47, the magnitude of the field vector whose potential is ϕ is $\partial\phi/\partial n$ (or $-\partial\phi/\partial n$ in the electrical and hydrodynamical cases). It follows that ϕ increases (or decreases) steadily as we move along a field line. Hence the field lines due to a single-valued potential cannot form closed curves in a simply connected space, for this would imply that ϕ had a series of values at a given point.

It follows from this that if $\partial\phi/\partial n$ be zero at every point on a closed boundary within which $\nabla^2\phi = 0$ at every point, then ϕ must have a constant value within this boundary. For, no field lines can cross the boundary, no field lines can begin or end within the boundary, and field lines cannot form closed curves within the boundary. Hence there are no field lines inside the boundary, which shows that $\partial\phi/\partial n = 0$ everywhere inside. In other words, ϕ must be constant within the boundary.

Further, if a region is enclosed partly by surfaces Σ_1 over which ϕ has a constant value, and partly by surfaces Σ_2 over which $\partial\phi/\partial n = 0$, then ϕ is a constant within the region. For no field lines can cross Σ_2, and none can connect two points on Σ_1, none can begin or end in the region, nor can the field lines form closed curves. There are therefore no field lines and so ϕ must be a constant within this region.

Let ϕ and ϕ' be two continuous solutions of Laplace's equation, both of which are finite and one-valued at all points of a given region which is enclosed partly by surfaces Σ_1 over which $\phi = \phi'$ and partly by surfaces Σ_2 over which $\partial\phi/\partial n = \partial\phi'/\partial n$. The function $\Phi = \phi - \phi'$ is finite, one-valued and continuous at all points of the region. Further Φ has the constant value zero at all points on the surfaces Σ_1 and $\partial\Phi/\partial n$ is zero at all points on the surfaces Σ_2. We deduce that Φ has a constant value at all points of the region and that this constant is zero unless there are no surfaces Σ_1 present. It follows that at all points of the region,

$$\phi = \phi'$$

except in the case just mentioned, when $\phi = \phi' + \text{constant}$. This is the important **uniqueness theorem** which states that *if at each point of the boundary of a given region either ϕ or $\partial\phi/\partial n$ is known and if Laplace's equation is satisfied at each point in the region, then there is only one function ϕ which satisfies the given conditions, unless ϕ is not known at any point, in which case ϕ is indeterminate to the extent of an additive constant.*

§ **79.** The potential at P due to a source m at O is m/OP, and the potential at P due to a source m at O' is $m/O'P$. The difference of these two potentials is

$$m(O'P - OP)/(OP)(O'P),$$

and the absolute value of this is never greater than $m(OO')/(OP)(O'P)$, so that as P recedes to an infinite distance from O and O', this difference eventually vanishes.

It follows that for distributions lying entirely within a finite closed surface, the potential of the distribution approaches more and more closely to the potential due to a single point source as we move further and further away from the distribution, the strength of the point source being the net algebraic source strength within the surface.

§ 80. We shall now gather together the important properties of the potential ϕ.

(i) When only surface and volume distributions are present, ϕ is continuous. ϕ has a singularity at a point source. $\ldots$ § 62, § 63

(ii) ϕ is discontinuous across a magnetic shell and

$$\phi_+ - \phi_- = 4\pi\tau \qquad\qquad \ldots\ldots\text{§ 64}$$

(iii) $\dfrac{\partial\phi}{\partial l}$ is continuous, except where a surface distribution or a surface of separation of two media is crossed.

$\ldots\ldots$ § 69 (26)

(iv) At a surface distribution or at a surface of separation

$$\kappa_1\left(\frac{\partial\phi}{\partial n}\right)_1 - \kappa_2\left(\frac{\partial\phi}{\partial n}\right)_2 = -4\pi\sigma, \qquad \ldots\ldots\text{§ 69 (25)}$$

where dn is in the direction of the normal to the surface drawn into side 1.

(v) At a surface distribution or at a surface of separation

$$\left(\frac{\partial\phi}{\partial t}\right)_1 = \left(\frac{\partial\phi}{\partial t}\right)_2, \qquad\qquad \ldots\ldots\text{§ 62 (9)}$$

where dt is tangential to the surface in question.

(vi) If κ is independent of position, then

$$\nabla^2\phi = -4\pi\rho/\kappa. \qquad\qquad \ldots\ldots\text{§ 69 (24)}$$

I

(vii) The potential ϕ of a finite distribution tends, at an infinite distance from the finite distribution, to the potential due to a point charge.   ....§ 79

(viii) For given boundary conditions there is only one solution to $\nabla^2\phi = 0$.   ....§ 78

The corresponding conditions in the gravitational and hydrodynamical cases are obtained by putting $\kappa = 1$ in (iv) and (vi).

§ 81. We now consider the following problem. If we are given the potential at all points can we find a source distribution which will give rise to this potential ? In the electrical case we suppose that the value of the dielectric constant at each point is also given. In the other cases we put $\kappa = 1$ in the following formulae. The volume density at any point is given by

$$\rho = -\frac{\kappa}{4\pi}\nabla^2\phi. \quad \cdot \quad \cdot \quad \cdot \quad \cdot \quad (1)$$

Surface distributions will be found at points where $\kappa(\partial\phi/\partial n)$ has a discontinuity. The surface density will be

$$\sigma = -\frac{1}{4\pi}\left(\kappa_1\frac{\partial\phi_1}{\partial n} - \kappa_2\frac{\partial\phi_2}{\partial n}\right). \quad \cdot \quad \cdot \quad (2)$$

Point sources can only occur when ϕ has a singularity. The strength of such a source is found by applying Gauss's Law to a small surface (usually a sphere) surrounding the singularity. Thus

$$m = -\frac{1}{4\pi}\int\kappa\frac{\partial\phi}{\partial n}ds, \quad \cdot \quad \cdot \quad \cdot \quad (3)$$

where m represents the charge or source strength or mass as the case may be.

Magnetic shells can be found on surfaces at which ϕ is discontinuous. The dipole strength per unit area is

$$\tau = \frac{1}{4\pi}(\phi_1 \sim \phi_2)$$

the source side being the one with the greater value of ϕ.

The distribution corresponding to a given potential is not unique if we admit the existence of volume distributions of dipoles. This will be clear from § 64.

We shall apply the above to the following example. Suppose that the gravitational potential is given by

$$\phi_1 = 2\pi(b^2 - a^2) \qquad \text{if} \quad 0 < r < a,$$

$$\phi_2 = \frac{2}{3}\pi\left(3b^2 - r^2 - \frac{2a^3}{r}\right) \quad \text{if} \quad a < r < b,$$

$$\phi_3 = \frac{4}{3}\pi\left(\frac{b^3 - a^3}{r}\right) \qquad \text{if} \quad b < r.$$

We observe that ϕ has no singularities, so no point charges are present. Again, since it is easily verified that ϕ is continuous, we conclude that no magnetic shells are present.

Now $\nabla^2\phi_1 = 0$ since ϕ_1 is a constant. Also $\nabla^2\phi_3 = 0$ for we can show that $\nabla^2(1/r) = 0$. Now $\nabla^2\phi_2 = \nabla^2(-\frac{2}{3}\pi r^2)$, for the other terms vanish, and $\nabla^2(r^2) = 6$, so $\nabla^2\phi_2 = -4\pi$. The only volume distribution is between the concentric spheres $r = a$ and $r = b$ and this is a distribution of unit density.

It is easy to see that

$$\frac{\partial\phi_1}{\partial r} = 0, \quad \frac{\partial\phi_2}{\partial r} = \frac{2}{3}\pi\left(-2r + \frac{2a^3}{r^2}\right), \quad \frac{\partial\phi_3}{\partial r} = -\frac{4}{3}\pi\left(\frac{b^3 - a^3}{r^2}\right).$$

Hence the surface distribution at $r = a$ is

$$-\frac{1}{4\pi}\left\{\left(\frac{\partial\phi_2}{\partial r}\right)_{r=a} - \left(\frac{\partial\phi_1}{\partial r}\right)_{r=a}\right\} = 0,$$

and the surface distribution at $r = b$ is

$$-\frac{1}{4\pi}\left\{\left(\frac{\partial\phi_3}{\partial r}\right)_{r=b} - \left(\frac{\partial\phi_2}{\partial r}\right)_{r=b}\right\} = 0.$$

Hence there are no surface distributions.

The answer to our problem is that there is matter of unit density between the shells $r = a$ and $r = b$, but that no other matter is present. The total mass present is therefore $\frac{4}{3}\pi(b^3 - a^3)$. The potential of a particle of this mass situated at the origin would be $\frac{4}{3}\pi(b^3 - a^3)/r$. This is equal to the given potential at infinity, and so we have a check on our result.

§ 82. If we know the nature and location of all the distributions present the potential may be calculated from the formulae of § 63 and § 64, but if we are only told the magnitude of a charge on a conductor we do not know its location and the above method cannot be applied. The general problem of electrostatics is as follows. We may expect a number of dielectrics to be present and that κ is known for each. A number of conductors may be present and for each *either* ϕ is specified, *or* the total charge is specified, i.e., $\dfrac{-1}{4\pi}\displaystyle\int \kappa \dfrac{\partial \phi}{\partial n} ds$ is known. The magnitude and distribution of fixed charges are supposed to be known. The problem will involve finding a solution of Laplace's equation

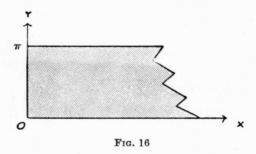

FIG. 16

or of Poisson's equation which satisfies certain conditions. The methods available for finding solutions to Laplace's equation will be illustrated by the examples of the following paragraphs. It will be observed that these methods are only applicable when the solution can be expressed as a product of functions each involving only one variable.

§ 83. Consider a very long strip of metal of breadth π with insulated sides. Let its two edges be kept at zero temperature and let one end be kept at known temperatures which are given functions of position on that end (fig. 16).

It may be shown that when the flow of heat is steady and the conductivity and specific heat per unit volume are constant, the temperature ϕ satisfies $\nabla^2\phi = 0$. The boundary conditions are $\phi = 0$ when $y = 0$ or π, and $\phi = f(y)$ when $x = 0$, where $f(y)$ is defined in the range $0 < y < \pi$.

We try to find a solution $\phi = XY$ where X is a function of x only and Y is a function of y only. If such a solution can be found, then by the uniqueness theorem it is the only one. Substituting $\phi = XY$ in $\nabla^2\phi = 0$, we have

$$X''Y + Y''X = 0,$$

so that $\qquad\qquad X''/X = -Y''/Y.$

Now X''/X cannot involve y and Y''/Y cannot involve x so both of these quantities must be equal to a constant which we call n^2. We have thus two equations to solve:

$$X'' - n^2X = 0, \quad Y'' + n^2Y = 0 ;$$

whence, apart from constants,

$$X = e^{nx} \quad \text{or} \quad e^{-nx}, \quad Y = \cos ny \text{ or } \sin ny.$$

The most general solution is therefore

$$\phi = \sum_n (A_ne^{nx} + B_ne^{-nx})(C_n \cos ny + D_n \sin ny) \quad . \quad (4)$$

But $\phi = 0$ when $y = 0$ so all the C's are zero, and $\phi = 0$ when $y = \pi$, so n must be an integer. Also ϕ is never infinite so the A's are all zero. Thus

$$\phi = \sum_n a_ne^{-nx} \sin ny ;$$

putting $x = 0$, we obtain

$$\phi_{x=0} = \sum_n a_n \sin ny.$$

The values of the a's may now be obtained by comparing this function with the known function $f(y)$. We have only to express $f(y)$ as a Fourier series in sines of integral multiples of y and the a's can then be determined. E.g., if we are given $f(y) = \sin y + 2 \sin 3y$, then $a_1 = 1$, $a_3 = 2$ and the other a's are zero so that the solution is $\phi = e^{-x} \sin y + 2e^{-3x} \sin 3y$.

§ 84. It is important to obtain a solution of Laplace's equation which is symmetrical about an axis. If we choose this as the z axis, and choose spherical polar coordinates then the potential ϕ will be independent of the coordinate ψ. Laplace's equation then takes the form

$$\frac{\partial}{\partial r}\left(r^2 \frac{\partial \phi}{\partial r}\right) + \frac{1}{\sin \theta} \frac{\partial}{\partial \theta}\left(\sin \theta \frac{\partial \phi}{\partial \theta}\right) = 0.$$

Try $\phi = R\Theta$, where R is a function of r only and Θ is a function of θ only. Then

$$\frac{1}{R} \frac{\partial}{\partial r}\left(r^2 \frac{\partial R}{\partial r}\right) = -\frac{1}{\Theta \sin \theta} \frac{\partial}{\partial \theta}\left(\sin \theta \frac{\partial \Theta}{\partial \theta}\right).$$

The left-hand side cannot involve θ and the right-hand side cannot involve r, so both sides must be equal to a constant which we shall write as $n(n+1)$ for convenience. We have now to solve the two equations

$$\frac{\partial}{\partial r}\left(r^2 \frac{\partial R}{\partial r}\right) - n(n+1)R = 0, \quad \frac{\partial}{\partial \theta}\left(\sin \theta \frac{\partial \Theta}{\partial \theta}\right) + n(n+1)\,\Theta \sin \theta = 0$$

The solution of the first is

$$R = A_n r^n + B_n r^{-(n+1)}.$$

The second equation takes the form

$$\frac{\partial}{\partial \mu}\left\{(1-\mu^2)\frac{\partial \Theta}{\partial \mu}\right\} + n(n+1)\Theta = 0,$$

when we put $\mu = \cos \theta$. This is Legendre's equation * of order n and its solution is

$$\Theta = C_n P_n(\mu) + D_n Q_n(\mu),$$

where C_n and D_n are constants, P_n is the Legendre function of degree n and $Q_n = P_n \int_\infty^\mu \frac{d\mu}{(\mu^2-1)P_n{}^2}$. The Q_n solutions can

* Ince, *Integration of Ordinary Differential Equations* (2nd edition), pp. 119-124.

usually be discarded as they have singularities on the z axis. It is well known * that P_n is the coefficient of t^n in the expansion of $(1 - 2\mu t + t^2)^{-\frac{1}{2}}$, so that

$$P_0 = 1, \quad P_1 = \mu, \quad P_2 = \tfrac{1}{2}(3\mu^2 - 1), \quad P_3 = \tfrac{1}{2}(5\mu^3 - 3\mu), \ldots$$

and it can be shown that these P's are linearly independent. The complete solution is now

$$\phi = \sum_n (A_n r^n + B_n r^{-(n+1)})(C_n P_n + D_n Q_n), \qquad . \qquad (5)$$

and to this solution we must apply the conditions given in any problem.

We shall apply this to the case of a dielectric sphere of radius q in a given uniform field of intensity F. Let ϕ_1 be the potential inside the sphere and ϕ_2 the potential outside the sphere. The conditions which we have to apply to the solution (5) are (i) $\nabla^2 \phi_1 = 0$ inside the sphere, (ii) $\nabla^2 \phi_2 = 0$ outside the sphere, (iii) $\phi_2 = -Fz = -Fr \cos \theta$ at large distances from the sphere, (iv) $\phi_1 = \phi_2$ when $r = q$, (v) $\kappa(\partial\phi_1/\partial r) = \partial\phi_2/\partial r$ when $r = q$. We can discard the Q_n solutions, so we assume

$$\phi_1 = \sum_n (A_n r^n + B_n r^{-(n+1)})P_n, \quad \phi_2 = \sum_n (C_n r^n + D_n r^{-(n+1)})P_n.$$

From (iii) all the C's must be zero except C_1. Also ϕ_1 can have no singularities within the sphere, so all the B's are zero. Hence

$$\phi_1 = \sum_n A_n r^n P_n, \quad \phi_2 = C_1 r P_1 + \sum_n D_n r^{-(n+1)} P_n.$$

From (iv)

$$C_1 q P_1 + \sum_n D_n q^{-(n+1)} P_n = \sum_n A_n q^n P_n,$$

but since the P's are linearly independent,

$$C_1 q + D_1/q^2 = A_1 q, \qquad . \qquad . \qquad . \qquad . \qquad (6)$$

and $\quad\quad\quad\quad D_n q^{-(n+1)} = A_n q^n, \quad (n \neq 1). \qquad . \qquad . \qquad (7)$

* Whittaker and Watson, *Modern Analysis*, chap. xv.

From (v)

$$C_1 P_1 - \sum_n (n+1) D_n q^{-(n+2)} P_n = \kappa \sum_n n A_n q^{n-1} P_n,$$

whence

$$C_1 - 2D_1/q^3 = \kappa A_1, \qquad . \qquad . \qquad . \qquad (8)$$

and

$$-(n+1) D_n q^{-(n+2)} = \kappa n A_n q^{n-1}, \quad (n \neq 1). \qquad . \qquad (9)$$

From (7) and (9) we see that $A_n = D_n = 0$ if $n \neq 1$.
From (iii) $C_1 = -F$ so (6) and (8) become

$$-F + D_1/q^3 = A_1, \quad F + 2D_1/q^3 = -\kappa A_1,$$

so on solving these two equations

$$A_1 = -\frac{3F}{\kappa+2}, \quad D_1 = q^3 F \frac{(\kappa-1)}{(\kappa+2)}.$$

We have now determined all the constants, and the solution required is

$$\phi_1 = -\frac{3F}{\kappa+2} r \cos \theta = -\frac{3Fz}{\kappa+2},$$

$$\phi_2 = -Fr \cos \theta + \frac{q^3 F}{r^2}\left(\frac{\kappa-1}{\kappa+2}\right) \cos \theta = -Fz\left(1 - \frac{q^3(\kappa-1)}{r^3(\kappa+2)}\right).$$

§ 85. The **wave equation** *

$$\frac{1}{c^2} \frac{\partial^2 z}{\partial t^2} = \frac{\partial^2 z}{\partial x^2} + \frac{\partial^2 z}{\partial y^2}$$

for the vibrations of a stretched membrane bears a very close resemblance to Laplace's equation and may be solved by similar methods. An investigation of the problem of a circular membrane of radius a fixed at its rim will throw an interesting side-light on the previous paragraphs. In the above equation c is a constant and t represents the time. The membrane is stretched in the XY plane so that z, which is a function of x, y, and t, represents the displacement per-

* An extensive treatment of this equation is given in Coulson, *Waves*, chap. i.

pendicular to the XY plane of any point on the membrane at any instant. We change to polar coordinates so that the wave equation takes the form

$$\frac{1}{c^2}\frac{\partial^2 z}{\partial t^2} = \frac{\partial^2 z}{\partial r^2} + \frac{1}{r}\frac{\partial z}{\partial r} + \frac{1}{r^2}\frac{\partial^2 z}{\partial \theta^2}.$$

We assume a solution $z = R\Theta T$, where $R = R(r)$, $\Theta = \Theta(\theta)$, $T = T(t)$. This done, we have

$$\frac{1}{c^2}T''R\Theta = \Theta T\left(R'' + \frac{1}{r}R'\right) + \frac{1}{r^2}RT\Theta''$$

or

$$\frac{1}{c^2}\frac{T''}{T} = \frac{R''}{R} + \frac{1}{r}\frac{R'}{R} + \frac{1}{r^2}\frac{\Theta''}{\Theta}.$$

Since the right-hand side is independent of t, it must be a constant which we shall take to be $-n^2$. (We take the negative sign because we expect T to be periodic.) Hence

$$r^2\frac{R''}{R} + r\frac{R'}{R} + n^2r^2 = -\frac{\Theta''}{\Theta}.$$

As before we see that both sides are equal to a constant which we call k^2. We have therefore three equations to solve, viz.

$$r^2R'' + rR' + (n^2r^2 - k^2)R = 0,$$
$$\Theta'' + k^2\Theta = 0, \qquad\qquad T'' + c^2n^2T = 0.$$

The first of these is Bessel's equation and its solutions are Bessel Functions.* If we choose the time origin and the initial line suitably, the solutions of these equations are respectively

$$R = AJ_k(nr) + BY_k(nr), \qquad \Theta = C\cos(k\theta). \qquad T = D\cos(cnt),$$

where $J_k(nr)$ and $Y_k(nr)$ are Bessel functions. J_k is finite but Y_k is infinite when $r = 0$, so we may usually discard the Y_k term. Hence

$$z = \sum_{n,k} a_{n,k} J_k(nr)\cos(k\theta)\cos(cnt). \qquad . \qquad (10)$$

We notice that k must be an integer in order that $\cos(k\theta)$

* Whittaker and Watson, *Modern Analysis*, chap. xvii, and Ince, *Integration of Ordinary Differential Equations* (2nd edition), pp. 124-129.

$= \cos (k\,\overline{\theta + 2\pi})$; also $z = 0$ when $r = a$, for all values of t and θ, hence

$$J_k(na) = 0.$$

This determines the values of n permissible for a given value of k. E.g., if $k = 0$, then $na/\pi = .7655$, 1.7571, $2.7546, \ldots$ We have still to determine the values of the constants $a_{n,k}$ from the value of z at $t = 0$, but this is beyond the scope of the present book.

Other wave equations may be treated in a similar manner.

§ 86.   Examples

(1) Find what distribution gives rise to the potentials $\phi_{r>a} = 4az/r^3$, $\phi_{r<a} = (3a^2 + 4az - 3r^2)/a^3$. [$\rho_{r>a} = 0$, $\rho_{r<a} = 9/2\pi a^3$, $\sigma = 3(2z - a)/2\pi a^3$.]

(2) A dielectric sphere (constant κ), which has a point charge $+e$ at its centre, is situated in free space. Show that $\phi_{r>a} = e/r$, $\phi_{r<a} = (e/\kappa)\{1/r + (\kappa - 1)/a\}$ where a is the radius of the sphere.

(3) A spherical conductor of radius a has a charge e and is situated in free space. Show that $\phi_{r>a} = e/r$ and $\phi_{r<a} = e/a$.

(4) A condenser consists of two coaxial and infinite cylindrical conductors of radii a and b, $(a > b)$ which are kept at potentials ϕ_a and ϕ_b. Show that

$$\phi_{b<r<a} = \{\phi_b \log a - \phi_a \log b + (\phi_a - \phi_b) \log r\}/(\log a - \log b).$$

(5) Solve the equation $\dfrac{1}{c^2} \dfrac{\partial^2 \phi}{\partial t^2} = \dfrac{\partial^2 \phi}{\partial x^2}$ subject to the conditions

$\phi_{x=0} = \phi_{x=l} = 0$, $\phi_{t=0} = \sin^3 (\pi x/l)$, $\left(\dfrac{\partial \phi}{\partial t}\right)_{t=0} = 0$. (This is the problem of finding the wave motion of a taut string fixed at two ends and initially at rest.)

$[\phi = \tfrac{1}{4}\{3 \sin (\pi x/l) \cos (\pi ct/l) - \sin (3\pi x/l) \cos (3\pi ct/l)\}.]$

(6) The problem of finding the velocity potential due to a sphere of radius a, moving with velocity V in a straight line through a liquid which is at rest at infinity, reduces to solving $\nabla^2 \phi = 0$ under the following conditions (i) ϕ does not involve ψ, (ii) $\phi_\infty = 0$, (iii) $\left(\dfrac{\partial \phi}{\partial r}\right)_{r=a} = - V \cos \theta$. Show that the stream lines are $r = c \sin^2 \theta$ and that $\phi = (a^3 V \cos \theta)/2r^2$.

CHAPTER VIII

FOUR-DIMENSIONAL VECTORS

§ 87. In this chapter we shall extend some of the ideas which we have developed in the previous chapters to the four-dimensional case. We shall use rectangular Cartesian coordinates x_1, x_2, x_3, x_4 and take $\mathbf{i}_1, \mathbf{i}_2, \mathbf{i}_3, \mathbf{i}_4$ to be unit vectors in the four coordinate directions. We shall use cursive type to denote a four-dimensional vector or a **world vector** as it is sometimes called, so that if the world vector $\mathcal{A}$ has components a_1, a_2, a_3, a_4, then we may write

$$\mathcal{A} \equiv a_1\mathbf{i}_1 + a_2\mathbf{i}_2 + a_3\mathbf{i}_3 + a_4\mathbf{i}_4.$$

Since the coordinate directions are mutually perpendicular we have

$$\mathbf{i}_j \cdot \mathbf{i}_j = 1, \quad \mathbf{i}_j \cdot \mathbf{i}_k = 0 \quad (j \neq k),$$

so that

$$\mathcal{A} \cdot \mathcal{B} \equiv a_1b_1 + a_2b_2 + a_3b_3 + a_4b_4. \quad \bullet \quad \bullet \quad (1)$$

Returning for a moment to the three-dimensional case, we remark that $\mathbf{a} \times \mathbf{b}$ has three components which are more accurately described by pairs of suffixes than by single ones. We can write in fact

$$c_{23} = a_2b_3 - a_3b_2 = -c_{32},$$
$$c_{31} = a_3b_1 - a_1b_3 = -c_{13},$$
$$c_{12} = a_1b_2 - a_2b_1 = -c_{21},$$

and arrange the c's as the elements of the anti-symmetric matrix

$$\begin{bmatrix} \cdot & c_{12} & c_{13} \\ c_{21} & \cdot & c_{23} \\ c_{31} & c_{32} & \cdot \end{bmatrix},$$

where the element in the jth row and kth column is $c_{jk} = a_j b_k - a_k b_j$. In an analogous manner we can define the vector product $\mathcal{A} \times \mathcal{B}$ of two world vectors as an antisymmetric matrix of four rows and columns

$$\mathcal{A} \times \mathcal{B} \equiv \begin{bmatrix} . & c_{12} & c_{13} & c_{14} \\ c_{21} & . & c_{23} & c_{24} \\ c_{31} & c_{32} & . & c_{34} \\ c_{41} & c_{42} & c_{43} & . \end{bmatrix}, \quad . \quad . \quad (2)$$

and it will be observed that only six of the c's are independent. $\mathcal{A} \times \mathcal{B}$ is not therefore a world vector.

§ **88.** The frequent use which we have already made of the operator ∇ leads us to consider the world vector operator

$$\square \equiv \mathbf{i}_1 \frac{\partial}{\partial x_1} + \mathbf{i}_2 \frac{\partial}{\partial x_2} + \mathbf{i}_3 \frac{\partial}{\partial x_3} + \mathbf{i}_4 \frac{\partial}{\partial x_4}.$$

If Φ be a scalar function of x_1, x_2, x_3, x_4, then

$$\text{grad } \Phi \equiv \square \Phi = \frac{\partial \Phi}{\partial x_1} \mathbf{i}_1 + \frac{\partial \Phi}{\partial x_2} \mathbf{i}_2 + \frac{\partial \Phi}{\partial x_3} \mathbf{i}_3 + \frac{\partial \Phi}{\partial x_4} \mathbf{i}_4 \quad . \quad (3)$$

Further

$$\text{div } \mathcal{A} \equiv \square . \mathcal{A} = \frac{\partial a_1}{\partial x_1} + \frac{\partial a_2}{\partial x_2} + \frac{\partial a_3}{\partial x_3} + \frac{\partial a_4}{\partial x_4}, \quad . \quad (4)$$

so that

$$\text{div grad } \Phi \equiv \square^2 \Phi = \frac{\partial^2 \Phi}{\partial x_1{}^2} + \frac{\partial^2 \Phi}{\partial x_2{}^2} + \frac{\partial^2 \Phi}{\partial x_3{}^2} + \frac{\partial^2 \Phi}{\partial x_4{}^2}. \quad . \quad (5)$$

The expression for curl $\mathcal{A}$ will, however, be an anti-symmetric matrix and in fact

$$\text{curl } \mathcal{A} \equiv \square \times \mathcal{A} = \begin{bmatrix} . & b_{12} & b_{13} & b_{14} \\ b_{21} & . & b_{23} & b_{24} \\ b_{31} & b_{32} & . & b_{34} \\ b_{41} & b_{42} & b_{43} & . \end{bmatrix} \quad . \quad (6)$$

where

$$b_{jk} \equiv \frac{\partial a_k}{\partial x_j} - \frac{\partial a_j}{\partial x_k} . \quad . \quad . \quad . \quad . \quad (7)$$

It follows that all the elements of

$$\text{curl grad } \Phi \equiv \Box \times (\Box \Phi)$$

are identically zero, just as all the components of $\nabla \times (\nabla \phi)$ are zero. Corresponding to the identity

$$\nabla \cdot (\nabla \times \mathbf{a}) \equiv 0,$$

we have four identities

$$\left. \begin{array}{ll} \dfrac{\partial b_{34}}{\partial x_2} + \dfrac{\partial b_{42}}{\partial x_3} + \dfrac{\partial b_{23}}{\partial x_4} \equiv 0, & \dfrac{\partial b_{34}}{\partial x_1} + \dfrac{\partial b_{41}}{\partial x_3} + \dfrac{\partial b_{13}}{\partial x_4} \equiv 0, \\[3mm] \dfrac{\partial b_{24}}{\partial x_1} + \dfrac{\partial b_{41}}{\partial x_2} + \dfrac{\partial b_{12}}{\partial x_4} \equiv 0, & \dfrac{\partial b_{23}}{\partial x_1} + \dfrac{\partial b_{31}}{\partial x_2} + \dfrac{\partial b_{12}}{\partial x_3} \equiv 0, \end{array} \right\} . \quad (8)$$

where b_{jk} is defined by (7).

If we regard the kth row $b_{k1}, b_{k2}, b_{k3}, b_{k4}$ of an anti-symmetric matrix as a world vector $\mathcal{B}_k$, then we can define $\Box \cdot (\Box \times \mathcal{A})$ as the vector

$$(\Box \cdot \mathcal{B}_1)\mathbf{i}_1 + (\Box \cdot \mathcal{B}_2)\mathbf{i}_2 + (\Box \cdot \mathcal{B}_3)\mathbf{i}_3 + (\Box \cdot \mathcal{B}_4)\mathbf{i}_4.$$

Now the kth component is

$$\begin{aligned}
\Box \cdot \mathcal{B}_k &= \frac{\partial b_{k1}}{\partial x_1} + \frac{\partial b_{k2}}{\partial x_2} + \frac{\partial b_{k3}}{\partial x_3} + \frac{\partial b_{k4}}{\partial x_4} \\
&= \frac{\partial}{\partial x_1}\left(\frac{\partial a_1}{\partial x_k} - \frac{\partial a_k}{\partial x_1}\right) + \frac{\partial}{\partial x_2}\left(\frac{\partial a_2}{\partial x_k} - \frac{\partial a_k}{\partial x_2}\right) + \frac{\partial}{\partial x_3}\left(\frac{\partial a_3}{\partial x_k} - \frac{\partial a_k}{\partial x_3}\right) \\
&\qquad\qquad + \frac{\partial}{\partial x_4}\left(\frac{\partial a_4}{\partial x_k} - \frac{\partial a_k}{\partial x_4}\right) \\
&= \frac{\partial}{\partial x_k}\left(\frac{\partial a_1}{\partial x_1} + \frac{\partial a_2}{\partial x_2} + \frac{\partial a_3}{\partial x_3} + \frac{\partial a_4}{\partial x_4}\right) - \left(\frac{\partial^2 a_k}{\partial x_1^2} + \frac{\partial^2 a_k}{\partial x_2^2} + \frac{\partial^2 a_k}{\partial x_3^2} + \frac{\partial^2 a_k}{\partial x_4^2}\right) \\
&= \frac{\partial}{\partial x_k}(\Box \cdot \mathcal{A}) - \Box^2 a_k.
\end{aligned}$$

Hence

$$\Box \,.\,(\Box \times \mathcal{A}) = \Box(\Box \,.\, \mathcal{A}) - \Box^2 \mathcal{A}. \qquad \bullet \qquad \bullet \qquad (9)$$

§ 89. Euclidean geometry requires that the value of

$$dx^2 + dy^2 + dz^2$$

remains unaltered if we replace the axes $OXYZ$ by another unitary orthogonal system. The special theory of relativity is based on the supposition that the value of

$$dx^2 + dy^2 + dz^2 - c^2 dt^2$$

is invariant under a unitary orthogonal transformation of axes. In this last expression t represents the time and c is a constant which is identified with the velocity of light. We are thus led to consider a four-dimensional world with coordinates

$$x_1 = x, \quad x_2 = y, \quad x_3 = z, \quad x_4 = ict,$$

such that

$$dl^2 = dx_1{}^2 + dx_2{}^2 + dx_3{}^2 + dx_4{}^2.$$

In the remaining paragraphs we shall describe how some of the more important laws of physics can be formulated in terms of this four-dimensional coordinate system. Space, however, does not permit of more than a cursory investigation of these laws.

§ 90. The reader who is familiar with the theory of electricity will recall that in the Lorentz form the equations of the electromagnetic field may be written:

$$\nabla \,.\, \mathbf{E} = 4\pi\rho, \qquad \bullet \qquad \bullet \qquad (10) \qquad \nabla \times \mathbf{E} = -\frac{1}{c}\frac{\partial \mathbf{B}}{\partial t}, \qquad \bullet \qquad \bullet \qquad (11)$$

$$\nabla \,.\, \mathbf{B} = 0, \qquad \bullet \qquad \bullet \qquad \bullet \qquad (12) \qquad \nabla \times \mathbf{B} = \frac{1}{c}\left(4\pi\mathbf{J} + \frac{\partial \mathbf{E}}{\partial t}\right), \qquad (13)$$

$$\nabla \,.\, \mathbf{A} + \frac{1}{c}\frac{\partial \phi}{\partial t} = 0, \qquad \bullet \qquad (14) \qquad \nabla \,.\, \mathbf{J} + \frac{\partial \rho}{\partial t} = 0, \qquad \bullet \qquad \bullet \qquad (15)$$

$$\nabla^2 \mathbf{A} - \frac{1}{c^2}\frac{\partial^2 \mathbf{A}}{\partial t^2} = -\frac{4\pi}{c}\mathbf{J}, \qquad (16) \qquad \nabla^2 \phi - \frac{1}{c^2}\frac{\partial^2 \phi}{\partial t^2} = -4\pi\rho, \qquad \bullet \qquad (17)$$

where

$$\mathbf{B} \equiv \nabla \times \mathbf{A}, \quad . \quad . \quad . \quad (18) \qquad \mathbf{E} \equiv -\nabla\phi - \frac{1}{c}\frac{\partial \mathbf{A}}{\partial t}. \qquad (19)$$

The significances of the symbols employed are as follows :

$\mathbf{A}$ = vector potential, ϕ = scalar potential,

$\mathbf{B}$ = magnetic induction, $\mathbf{E}$ = electric intensity,

$\mathbf{J}$ = current density, ρ = charge density.

Evidently we may write (14) and (15) as

$$\square \, . \, \mathcal{A} = 0, \quad \square \, . \, \mathcal{J} = 0$$

respectively, if we define $\mathcal{A}$ and $\mathcal{J}$ by

$$\mathcal{A} \equiv A_x\mathbf{i}_1 + A_y\mathbf{i}_2 + A_z\mathbf{i}_3 + i\phi\mathbf{i}_4,$$
$$\mathcal{J} \equiv \{J_x\mathbf{i}_1 + J_y\mathbf{i}_2 + J_z\mathbf{i}_3 + ic\rho\mathbf{i}_4\}4\pi/c.$$

If b_{ij} are the elements of the anti-symmetric matrix for $\square \times \mathcal{A}$, then it is evident from equations (18) and (19), which define $\mathbf{B}$ and $\mathbf{E}$, that

$$b_{23} = B_x, \qquad b_{31} = B_y, \qquad b_{12} = B_z,$$
$$b_{14} = -iE_x, \quad b_{24} = -iE_y, \quad b_{34} = -iE_z.$$

Hence

$$\square \times \mathcal{A} = \begin{bmatrix} . & B_z & -B_y & -iE_x \\ -B_z & . & B_x & -iE_y \\ B_y & -B_x & . & -iE_z \\ iE_x & iE_y & iE_z & . \end{bmatrix}.$$

The identities (8) now take the form

$$0 \equiv -\frac{\partial(iE_z)}{\partial y} + \frac{\partial(iE_y)}{\partial z} + \frac{\partial(B_x)}{ic\,\partial t} = -i\left[\left(\frac{\partial E_z}{\partial y} - \frac{\partial E_y}{\partial z}\right) + \frac{1}{c}\frac{\partial B_x}{\partial t}\right],$$

$$0 \equiv -\frac{\partial(iE_z)}{\partial x} + \frac{\partial(iE_x)}{\partial z} + \frac{\partial(-B_y)}{ic\,\partial t} = \ \ i\left[\left(\frac{\partial E_x}{\partial z} - \frac{\partial E_z}{\partial x}\right) + \frac{1}{c}\frac{\partial B_y}{\partial t}\right],$$

$$0 \equiv -\frac{\partial(iE_y)}{\partial x} + \frac{\partial(iE_x)}{\partial y} + \frac{\partial B_z}{ic\,\partial t} = -i\left[\left(\frac{\partial E_y}{\partial x} - \frac{\partial E_x}{\partial y}\right) + \frac{1}{c}\frac{\partial B_z}{\partial t}\right],$$

$$0 \equiv \frac{\partial B_x}{\partial x} + \frac{\partial B_y}{\partial y} + \frac{\partial B_z}{\partial z} \equiv \nabla \, . \, \mathbf{B}.$$

These identities are therefore summed up in the equations

$$\nabla \times \mathbf{E} + \frac{1}{c}\frac{\partial \mathbf{B}}{\partial t} = 0, \quad \nabla \cdot \mathbf{B} = 0,$$

which are precisely equations (12) and (11).

Equations (16) and (17) may be combined into the single equation
$$\Box^2 \mathcal{A} = -\mathcal{J}.$$

Since $\Box \cdot \mathcal{A} = 0$ it follows from (9) that

$$\Box \cdot (\Box \times \mathcal{A}) = \mathcal{J}.$$

This is simply a combination of (10) and (13) as we shall now verify.

The divergence of the first row of $\Box \times \mathcal{A}$ is

$$\frac{\partial}{\partial y}(B_z) + \frac{\partial}{\partial z}(-B_y) + \frac{1}{ic}\frac{\partial}{\partial t}(-iE_x) = (\nabla \times \mathbf{B})_x - \frac{1}{c}\frac{\partial}{\partial t}E_x.$$

The divergences of the second and third rows are

$$(\nabla \times \mathbf{B})_y - \frac{1}{c}\frac{\partial}{\partial t}E_y, \quad (\nabla \times \mathbf{B})_z - \frac{1}{c}\frac{\partial}{\partial t}E_z,$$

while the divergence of the fourth is

$$i\left[\frac{\partial}{\partial x}E_x + \frac{\partial}{\partial y}E_y + \frac{\partial}{\partial z}E_z\right] = i\nabla \cdot \mathbf{E}.$$

By (13) and (10) these are respectively $\dfrac{4\pi}{c}J_x$, $\dfrac{4\pi}{c}J_y$, $\dfrac{4\pi}{c}J_z$, $i4\pi\rho$, which are the components of $\mathcal{J}$.

§ **91.** In Newtonian mechanics we have

$$x' = x - Vt, \quad y' = y, \quad z' = z, \qquad . \qquad . \quad (20)$$

where $O'X'Y'Z'$ are axes parallel to $OXYZ$ which are moving with uniform velocity V in the direction OX relative to the fixed axial system $OXYZ$. For such a transformation, however,
$$dl^2 = dx^2 + dy^2 + dz^2 - c^2dt^2$$

is not invariant unless dt be zero. In the special theory of relativity we use in place of (20) the **Lorentz transformation**

$$x' = \beta(x - Vt), \quad y' = y, \quad z' = z, \quad t' = \beta\left(t - \frac{V}{c^2}x\right), \quad (21)$$

where $\beta = (1 - V^2/c^2)^{-\frac{1}{2}}$. It may be verified that this transformation leaves dl^2 invariant. If we write

$$v_x = \frac{dx}{dt}, \quad v_y = \frac{dy}{dt}, \quad v_z = \frac{dz}{dt},$$

$$v_x' = \frac{dx'}{dt'}, \quad v_y' = \frac{dy'}{dt'}, \quad v_z' = \frac{dz'}{dt'},$$

for the components of the velocity of a moving point P relative to the two axial systems, it may be shown that

$$v_x' = \gamma(v_x - V), \quad v_y' = \beta^{-1}\gamma v_y, \quad v_z' = \beta^{-1}\gamma v_z,$$

where $\gamma = (1 - v_x V/c^2)^{-1}$.

With these formulae, we find that the law of conservation of momentum, even if it hold for the axial system $OXYZ$, will not hold for the axial system $O'X'Y'Z'$. Since a law of nature cannot depend upon our choice of the axial system, we must modify our conception of momentum. Instead of taking

$$m\frac{dx}{dt}, \quad m\frac{dy}{dt}, \quad m\frac{dz}{dt},$$

let us take

$$m\frac{dx}{ds}, \quad m\frac{dy}{ds}, \quad m\frac{dz}{ds},$$

as the components of momentum, where

$$ds^2 = dt^2 - \frac{1}{c^2}(dx^2 + dy^2 + dz^2) = -\frac{1}{c^2}dl^2.$$

It is found that with this definition of momentum the law of conservation of momentum holds good for all axial

K

systems moving relative to one another with uniform velocity.

Now

$$m\frac{dx}{ds} = m\frac{dx}{dt}\frac{dt}{ds} = M\frac{dx}{dt},$$

where

$$M = m\frac{dt}{ds} = m\bigg/\frac{ds}{dt} = m/(1-v^2/c^2)^{\frac{1}{2}} = ma,$$

so that we may use the old definitions of momentum provided we replace the **rest mass** m by the **relative mass** M. The rest mass m is a permanent constant but the relative mass M increases with the velocity v. We observe that $M = m$ when $v = 0$. There is no appreciable difference between M and m when the velocity v is small compared with that of light.

We now consider the momentum world vector

$$\mathcal{M} \equiv m\Big(\frac{dx_1}{ds}\mathbf{i}_1 + \frac{dx_2}{ds}\mathbf{i}_2 + \frac{dx_3}{ds}\mathbf{i}_3 + \frac{dx_4}{ds}\mathbf{i}_4\Big)$$

$$\equiv m\Big(\frac{dx}{ds}\mathbf{i}_1 + \frac{dy}{ds}\mathbf{i}_2 + \frac{dz}{ds}\mathbf{i}_3 + ic\frac{dt}{ds}\mathbf{i}_4\Big).$$

When no external forces are acting the first three components are conserved. On examination we find that the fourth is also conserved. The fourth component is $icm\frac{dt}{ds}$ or icM. Hence the conservation of relative mass is the fourth component of the conservation of momentum. The conservation of M implies the conservation of $m/(1-v^2/c^2)^{\frac{1}{2}}$, or of $m(1 + \frac{1}{2}v^2/c^2)$ if v is small compared with c. But m is a permanent constant and so $\frac{1}{2}mv^2$ is conserved. Hence, for small velocities v, the fourth component of the conservation of momentum reduces to the conservation of Kinetic Energy.

§ 92. If we define force as the rate of change of momentum, then the x-component of the force is

$$X = \frac{d}{dt}\Big(m\frac{dx}{ds}\Big) = \frac{ds}{dt}m\frac{d}{ds}\Big(\frac{dx}{ds}\Big) = a^{-1}m\frac{d}{ds}\Big(\frac{dx}{ds}\Big).$$

The world vector representing the force will be

$$\mathcal{F} \equiv a^{-1}m \left[\frac{d}{ds}\left(\frac{dx}{ds}\right)\mathbf{i}_1 + \frac{d}{ds}\left(\frac{dy}{ds}\right)\mathbf{i}_2 + \frac{d}{ds}\left(\frac{dz}{ds}\right)\mathbf{i}_3 + ic\frac{d}{ds}\left(\frac{dt}{ds}\right)\mathbf{i}_4 \right],$$

the fourth component of which is proportional to the rate of change of relative mass. Let the velocity world vector be

$$\mathcal{V} \equiv \frac{dx}{ds}\mathbf{i}_1 + \frac{dy}{ds}\mathbf{i}_2 + \frac{dz}{ds}\mathbf{i}_3 + ic\frac{dt}{ds}\mathbf{i}_4.$$

Then

$$\mathcal{V} \cdot \mathcal{F} = \left\{\frac{dx}{ds}\frac{d}{ds}\left(\frac{dx}{ds}\right) + \frac{dy}{ds}\frac{d}{ds}\left(\frac{dy}{ds}\right) + \frac{dz}{ds}\frac{d}{ds}\left(\frac{dz}{ds}\right) - c^2\frac{dt}{ds}\frac{d}{ds}\left(\frac{dt}{ds}\right)\right\} a^{-1}m$$

$$= \tfrac{1}{2}ma^{-1}\frac{d}{ds}\left\{\left(\frac{dx}{ds}\right)^2 + \left(\frac{dy}{ds}\right)^2 + \left(\frac{dz}{ds}\right)^2 - c^2\left(\frac{dt}{ds}\right)^2\right\}$$

$$= \tfrac{1}{2}ma^{-1}\frac{d}{ds}\left(\frac{dl}{ds}\right)^2$$

$$= \tfrac{1}{2}ma^{-1}\frac{d}{ds}(-c^2)$$

$$= 0.$$

But

$$\mathcal{V} \cdot \mathcal{F} = \left(X\frac{dx}{ds} + Y\frac{dy}{ds} + Z\frac{dz}{ds}\right) - c^2\frac{dt}{ds}\frac{dM}{dt}$$

$$= \frac{dt}{ds}\left\{X\frac{dx}{dt} + Y\frac{dy}{dt} + Z\frac{dz}{dt} - c^2\frac{dM}{dt}\right\}.$$

So

$$X\frac{dx}{dt} + Y\frac{dy}{dt} + Z\frac{dz}{dt} = \frac{d}{dt}(Mc^2),$$

$$= \frac{d}{dt}(mc^2 + \tfrac{1}{2}mv^2 + \ldots.),$$

$$= \frac{d}{dt}(\tfrac{1}{2}mv^2),$$

if v is small compared with c. That is to say, *rate of doing work = rate of change of kinetic energy*. It follows that the conservation of energy theorem is expressed by the identity

$$\mathcal{V} \cdot \mathcal{F} \equiv 0.$$

BIBLIOGRAPHY

The following should be regarded as a selection rather than as a complete list of books for further study.

C. E. WEATHERBURN, Elementary Vector Analysis.
C. E. WEATHERBURN, Advanced Vector Analysis.
S. VALENTINER, Vektoranalysis.
L. BIEBERBACH, Analytische Geometrie.
C. E. WEATHERBURN, Differential Geometry of Three Dimensions.
W. BLASCHKE, Differentialgeometrie.
L. SILBERSTEIN, Vectorial Mechanics.
J. NIELSEN, Elementare Mechanik.
O. D. KELLOGG, Foundations of Potential Theory.
W. STERNBERG, Potentialtheorie.
M. ABRAHAM and R. BECKER, Classical Theory of Electricity and Magnetism.
G. H. LIVENS, The Theory of Electricity.
F. B. PIDDUCK, Lectures on the Mathematical Theory of Electricity.
L. M. MILNE-THOMSON, Theoretical Hydrodynamics.
C. A. COULSON, Waves.
W. V. HOUSTON, Principles of Mathematical Physics.
R. A. HOUSTOUN, Introduction to Mathematical Physics.
G. JOOS, Theoretical Physics.
T. M. MACROBERT, Spherical Harmonics.
J. RICE, Relativity, A Systematic Treatment, chap. 6.
W. H. McCREA, Relativity Physics.

INDEX

The numbers refer to the pages